KV-034-494

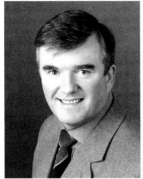

As Minister with responsibility for Services for Older People, I am delighted to receive the findings of this study, *The Role and Future Development of Day Services for Older People in Ireland*. I would like to congratulate all those involved in the preparation, compilation and production of this very worthwhile report.

The report brings together the findings of a qualitative exploration of the views of older people, service providers and carers on day services operated by the statutory and voluntary sectors.

As the population of older people in Ireland rises, there is an acceptance that they have been instrumental in building and strengthening the Irish economy to the healthy level we enjoy today. The present Government acknowledges their contribution to the economy and is fully committed to improving all aspects of the lives of older people by focusing on issues that affect their well-being, including health.

I am determined to ensure that all appropriate supports are in place so that the future direction of all services is client focused. I believe it is now my responsibility to work in a creative way to build on our achievements.

Ivor Callely TD
Minister for Services for Older People

The National Council on Ageing and Older People is very pleased to present this report, *The Role and Future Development of Day Services for Older People in Ireland.* It considers day services an integral component in the continuum of community care services for older people. It has consistently recommended that such services be designated as core services, underpinned by funding and legislation, so that all older persons are entitled to them as of right.

Day services are frequently mentioned in health board and government policy documents. However, day service provision has been characterised by under investment and limited strategic planning as noted in the *Value for Money Audit of the Irish Health System* (2001). In addition, the role that day services play in fulfilling government policy with respect to older people, and in honouring older people's own self-expressed wishes to remain in their own homes for as long as possible, has never been fully recognised.

The Council maintains that day services, if adequately resourced, have the potential to confer both health and social gains on members of our older population. It also proposes that the key to achieving these dual aims is to tailor services to the needs, preferences and abilities of older people. A prerequisite for the delivery of person-centred services is consultation with key players to identify the range of services that they may require. The research carried out for this report allowed older people, their carers and service providers to express their opinions for the first time about the perceived role and benefits of day services, about how services are currently delivered, about gaps in current service provision and about considerations for the future development of day services.

The Council believes that this report is timely, given the current shift of emphasis towards home care and community services for older people, as demonstrated in *Quality and Fairness: A Health System for You* (2001). It hopes that the report will facilitate the adoption of a more strategic approach to the planning and delivery of day services by identifying what the service objectives of different day services 'on the ground' should be, by detailing the components of service delivery required to achieve those objectives and by providing direction with regard to the evaluation of day services. The Council hopes that this report will act as a source of support to service planners and providers who seek to promote health and social gain of older people.

On behalf of the Council I would like to thank the author, Dr Deirdre Haslett, for her commitment and dedication in producing this excellent report. I would also like to thank Dr Ruth Loane who chaired the Council Consultative Committee that advised the progress of the research and oversaw the preparation of the report. Thanks are also due to the members of this Committee: Mr Noel Byrne, Ms Wendy Conroy, Ms Janet Convery, Ms Irene Feore, Ms Margaret Feeney, Dr John Gibbon, Mr John Grant, Ms Mary McDermott, Ms Mary O'Neill, Ms Mary Nally, Dr Helen McAvoy, Ms Frances O'Callaghan, Ms Hilary Scanlan and Ms Sinead Smith.

Finally, the Council would like to thank its Research Officer, Ms Sinead Quill, who steered the project on the Council's behalf. Special thanks are also due to Ms Gabrielle Jacob who prepared the report for publication and to the Council's administrative staff for their assistance throughout the course of the project.

Bob Carroll

Bob Carroll
Director

Author's acknowledgements

This study, *The Role and Future Development of Day Services for Older People in Ireland,* was commissioned by the National Council on Ageing and Older People (NCAOP).

The author would like to acknowledge the support and assistance of the staff of the Council, particularly Mr Bob Carroll, Director, Ms Sinead Quill, Research Officer and Dr Helen McAvoy, Healthy Ageing Programme Advisor. Thanks are also due to the members of the Consultative Committee who provided valuable feedback and guidance at different stages of the study.

Consultative Committee Members

Mr Noel Byrne	Westgate Foundation and Member, NCAOP
Ms Wendy Conroy	Policy Analyst, NCAOP
Ms Janet Convery	Director of Services for Older People, ECAHB and member, NCAOP*
Ms Irene Feore	Alzheimer Society of Ireland
Ms Margaret Feeney	Project Specialist, Services for Older People, MHB
Dr John Gibbon	Geriatrician (Retired) and member, NCAOP*
Mr John Grant	Western Alzheimer's Foundation and member, NCAOP
Ms Mary McDermott	Regional Director of Services for Older People, WHB and member, NCAOP*
Ms Mary O'Neill	Member, NCAOP
Ms Mary Nally	Summerhill Third Age Centre and member, NCAOP*
Dr Ruth Loane	Consultant in Old Age Psychiatry, MWHB and member, NCAOP
Dr Helen McAvoy	Healthy Ageing Programme Advisor, NCAOP
Ms Frances O'Callaghan	Projects Manager, Services for Older People, NEHB
Ms Hilary Scanlan	Care Group Co-ordinator for Older People, SHB
Ms Sinead Smith	NEHB

A very special thanks to the older people, their carers, the service providers and the Public Health Nurses who so generously gave of their time and who participated in the study with great enthusiasm.

* now former members

Contents

List of Tables

Council
Comments and
Recommendations

Council Comments and Recommendations

Government and health board policy documents have acknowledged the valuable role that day services play in providing services such as a midday meal, bath or shower, therapeutic and social services, and in promoting social contact and preventing loneliness, relieving caring relatives and providing social stimulation in a safe environment for older people with mild dementia (*The Years Ahead*, 1988). Day services may also reduce unnecessary admissions to institutional care, thereby keeping older people in their own homes for longer (North Eastern Health Board, 2001).

The National Council on Ageing and Older People proposes that the heterogeneity of the older population requires the provision of a continuum of day services that caters for the entire range of dependence levels. However, it notes that the provision of day services for older people in general has been characterised by inadequate funding and direction. In order for day services for older people to be developed strategically, the Council recommends that they be designated as core services with adequate dedicated funding and underpinned by the appropriate legislation, so that older people can access services by right or automatic entitlement.

2

The terminology used to describe different facilities is often confusing: one term may be used to describe two very different facilities and similarly, different terms are often applied to facilities that provide similar services (HeSSOP, 2001).[1] In order for day services for older people to be developed strategically and designated as core services, and for a continuum of day services to be established, the Council believes that the existing types of day service must be clearly defined.

The Council considers that one factor contributing to the ambiguous definitions of day services has been the lack of development of service objectives for different types of facilities. It believes that this has hampered the development of both day services and a continuum of day facilities appropriate to older people's diverse needs and preferences.

In order to define the service objectives for different types of day services, the Council felt that there was a need to know what older people themselves wanted and expected from the various services. In general, there is a lack of information about the people who use day services. The importance of tailoring health and social care services to individuals' needs and preferences is becoming increasingly recognised, and the Council believes that service objectives developed in isolation from a user perspective will not facilitate a person-centred approach to care delivery. This research obtains, for the first time, information from those using day facilities regarding the aspects of the facilities that they value the most.

In addition, consultations with service providers in the various types of centre, with Public Health Nurses and family carers, have directed the refinement of service objectives and definitions of day services in order to facilitate a more targeted response to the needs of older people.

---

1   The HeSSOP study noted that there was often 'inconsistency in terms of how these (day) services are defined and what particular services are provided'. This study found that there were day centres that could be classified as day care units because of the medical services offered there, while other day centres offered purely social activities.

Evaluation of health and social services, including day services for older people, has been limited until very recently and it is difficult to define standards for service delivery and to ascertain whether services are operating according to standards, without these evaluations. The importance of conducting service evaluations and local needs assessments is now acknowledged in government and health board policy documents as critical if services are to become more effective and appropriate to the needs of individual users and carers. This report proposes that existing centres should be evaluated against how well they achieve their service objectives. It is unique in providing, again for the first time, details of the structural and process components of service delivery necessary to achieve these service objectives and against which evaluations should be conducted.

Finally, the Council proposes that this report will assist service planners in allocating resources more efficiently and in establishing an appropriate range of day services within the wider continuum of community care for older people. One of the aims of the 2001 Health Strategy *Quality and Fairness* (Department of Health and Children, 2001, p81) is that 'the right care will be given, in the right place and at the right time'. The heterogeneity of older people means that a range of services will be required to meet their differing needs. The establishment of these services will ensure responsive and appropriate care delivery.

4

Classification/Definition of Services

Apart from day hospitals and psychiatric day hospitals, which are not considered in this report, the research has identified four broad categories of community-based day services for older people. The task of classification proved difficult because, for a number of reasons, a certain level of ambiguity exists with regard to day services for older people. This ambiguity also reflects a lack of strategic development in this sector.

Service objectives have been developed on the basis of consultations with service providers, older people and carers, the services offered and the characteristics of the members attending the centres. The centres are not defined by their present terms because, as noted earlier, present terminology is confusing and sometimes misleading. In addition, many services have names that reflect historical factors and therefore add little to the development of classifications. The following types of facility were identified in the research.

Dementia-Specific Day Centre

Investment in services for older people with dementia has been severely lacking in recent years, possibly because dementia has been seen as 'tomorrow's problem' (O'Shea and O'Reilly, 1999). However, the ageing of Ireland's population and, in particular, the increasing numbers of the 'very old', now requires a significant allocation of resources to dementia care given its higher prevalence rates in the older age categories. Dementia-specific day centres are rare and need to be expanded. The recent National Health Strategy (2001) has proposed that *An Action Plan for Dementia* (O'Shea and O'Reilly, 1999) will be implemented and the Council welcomes this proposal. The Council recommends that dementia-specific day centres be developed in the context of the recommendations made in *An Action Plan for Dementia* (1999). In this regard, the Council reiterates its recommendation that dementia-specific day places be provided in each district or community care area, in buildings suitable for people with dementia and with staff who are trained in their care.

Day Care Centre

In government and health board policy documents, references to day care usually relate to this model or type of day service and, as such, day care centre development has been given much more priority and direction than the other types of day services defined in the report. However, the Council is conscious that community services for older people are starting from a very low base and that investment in day care centres, although increasing in recent years, has been inadequate and incommensurate with the health and social gains that these centres could confer on older people. Therefore, the Council recommends that the number of day care centres be increased in the short- to medium-term. It is also eager to advocate that investing in the other types of day services detailed in this report should not be done at the expense of investment in day care centres. The Council proposes that each type of facility described in this report must be resourced fully to achieve its objectives.

Social Club/Day Centres

Social club/day centres often develop in response to a lack of other services in a particular area. For example, they may originally have been established to provide a day care service, but with few options for social interaction open to older people, particularly in rural areas, they have developed a more socially-oriented programme of activities for their more active clients. Similarly, a social club for older people may provide some therapeutic services in the absence of such services being available in the locality, or as the members' levels of dependency increase with age and the need for new services is identified. These centres are an integral component of the day services continuum: they are a direct product of local needs assessments and the unavailability of other resources and services.

These facilities were the most common type identified by the research. This is not surprising given the general under-investment in community services for older people and the spatial distribution of the older population which often results in an *ad hoc* local development of services. They have been called social club/day centres in this report because they provide many of the functions common to both. This name is also consistent with that proposed by the National Working Group on Performance Indicators. The Council recommends that social club/day centres be recognised as conferring both health and social gains, and that they be resourced adequately to fulfil their potential to do so.

Social Club

These clubs have previously been referred to in *The Years Ahead* (1988) and in health board policy documents for older people. However, they have never been given the recognition that they deserve for their role in empowering older people, health promotion, keeping older people active, promoting social inclusion and maintaining older people in their own homes for as long as possible. The Council recommends that social clubs be given full recognition as an integral element in the continuum of day services for older people. The allocation of core funding to these clubs by the health boards would signal an acknowledgement of their importance in promoting both health and social gains of older people.

Prerequisites for the Strategic Development of Day Services in Ireland

Ruddle *et al.* (1997) noted that day services have traditionally been one of the most neglected areas of community care for older people. The Council welcomes the inclusion of day services in the programme of the National Working Group on Performance Indicators, as this signals a shift in emphasis and an acknowledgement of the importance of this area of community care. In addition, the Council welcomes the recent National Health Strategy's (2001) commitment to establishing 7,000 extra day centre places over its lifetime. The Council considers this report to be timely, given this current shift of emphasis towards day services for older people, and believes that it will facilitate health and social service planners and providers to formulate a more strategic approach to the future development of day services in Ireland. It also proposes that the development of day services for older people will not be a strategic one unless the following areas, which have hitherto been neglected, are addressed.

1. Guidelines for the Operation and Management of Day Services

The Years Ahead (1988) recommended that the Department of Health prepare guidelines for the operation and management of day services, but to date such guidelines have not been produced. This has direct implications for the development of existing services and for the planning of future services. If day services are to be designated as core services their provision must be standardised and guidelines would facilitate this process. Therefore, the Council recommends that the Department of Health and Children use this report as a basis for the development of guidelines for the operation and management of the different types of facilities.

2. Terminology

The Council recommends that the terminology that has been developed for the various types of facility in this report, which is consistent with the definitions employed by the National Working Group on Performance Indicators, be adopted at a regional level by health boards and at a national level in government policy documents. While it is not essential that centres adopt this terminology at a local level (especially given the fact that some centres are so named for historical reasons), it is vital for planning purposes and the strategic development of day services that a standardised and consistent terminology be adopted.

3. Centres Should be Developed on Basis of the Revised Classification

The Council supports the National Health Strategy *Quality and Fairness* (2001) for the development of 7,000 additional day centre places, with the proviso that the full range of day services (including day care, social club/day centres, social clubs and dementia-specific day centres) be developed within each region/health board so that the needs of all older people, from the fully independent to those with high dependency levels, can be met.

4. Identification of the Types of Services Currently in Existence

It was noted during the preparation of the report that definitive lists of all day facilities are not available from the health boards at present, nor are national figures relating to the numbers of older people attending day services or accurate estimations of the numbers who may benefit from attending. The Council recommends that health boards conduct an audit of all day facilities available in their respective regions, whether provided in the voluntary, statutory or private sectors, and that directories of day services be made available to anyone wishing to access these services. Lists of the facilities or directories of day services should be available to all service providers and planners, so that they are in a position to refer older people to the facility most appropriate to their needs and preferences at a particular time. This proposal is consistent with Section 15 of the *Freedom of Information Act* that obliges health boards to make information about their services available to the public.

5. Clarification of the Term 'Day Service Place'

There is no clear definition of what constitutes a day service place. A hospital bed can be measured by its occupancy rate but a place in a day facility will depend on a number of factors such as staffing levels, physical space, ratio of staff to clients, dependency levels, services on offer and service objectives, among other things. According to the Department of Health and Children, a 'place' is defined as 'one day's care per person per week'. This implies that a day care centre that can accommodate twenty people per day is deemed to provide one hundred places. This definition does not give any direction with regard to the resources required to establish a day service place. The issue becomes more difficult when considering older people with different dependency levels. The resources required to provide a place in a dementia-specific day centre may not be the same as those required to provide a place in a day care centre, social club/day centre or a social club. The definition of the term 'day service place' has critical implications for the future development of day services, as well as for the planning of services and resource allocations required to achieve service objectives. The Council recommends that this question be addressed in the short-term.

8

6. Refinement of Recommended Numbers of Centres per Population

In *The Years Ahead* (1988) report it was noted that the Eastern Health Board (now the Eastern Regional Health Authority) recommended one day care centre for every three parishes and one social club for every parish in Ireland. The Council recommends that these figures should not be used as a benchmark for making recommendations about the number of centres per head of population of older people for the following reasons:

- the population of older people has risen significantly since 1988 when these figures were first developed. These increases have direct implications for the types and distribution of services that should be provided for older people

- the number of carers for older people has been falling in recent years. This implies that the services provided by statutory and voluntary organisations, including day services, will become more important to maintaining older people in their own homes

- the figures cited were developed by the Eastern Health Board. This was, and still is, the most populated health board area in Ireland. The use of such figures and averages does not, therefore, allow for regional disparities and spatial distribution issues. Some health board areas will have significantly greater numbers of older peoples than the average and others will have significantly fewer

- it was never recommended in *The Years Ahead* (1988) that these figures be used as a benchmark.

The Council believes that local and regional variations in the population density of older people, in current levels of service provision and in dependency levels, imply that the development of national benchmarks will not facilitate service development. In fact, anecdotal evidence suggests that the development of day services is built incrementally on existing services, unevenly distributed and is nowhere close to the figures mentioned in *The Years Ahead* (1988). The Council recommends that health boards endeavour to quantify the demand for the various day services in their respective regions. Figures should be based on an accurate analysis of need for these services. This analysis should pay particular attention to issues of spatial distribution and should also be cognisant of complementary services that may exist in a particular region. Any valid assessment of needs must include the views of older people themselves regarding their requirements and service preferences.

There is anecdotal evidence to suggest that health boards have very little expertise with regard to conducting needs analyses. The Council recommends that research be carried out to determine the most effective methodology for conducting needs analyses, as it would assist service planners and providers in adopting a more strategic and evidence-based approach to the provision of services for older people.

7. Responsibility for the Development of Day Services for Older People

There is currently no clear direction as to who should be responsible for the development of day services for older people in the community. The Council reiterates the recommendations of *The Years Ahead* (1988) that the health boards be legally obliged to provide and support day services for older people. The health boards should support voluntary organisations in the provision and management of these services if that is the wish of these organisations. Some voluntary organisations may have established their day services independently of health board input, and the health boards should encourage interested parties at community level to establish such services. The Council recommends that the health boards liaise with voluntary organisations to ensure that their day services operate according to the guidelines developed by the Department of Health and Children, as previously recommended.

Service Objectives for the Different Types of Facilities

It has been stated that one of the weaknesses in the provision of day services for older people has been that objectives have never been adequately developed in such a way as to give meaningful direction to service development. This has also had implications for the development of definitions of different types of facility. The Council acknowledges that day service staff are fully aware of the objectives of the services they provide and the role that they play in maintaining older people at home, in ensuring their health and social gains and in providing relief to carers. However, policy documents have rarely differentiated between the various elements in the continuum of day services and tend to group them all under the term 'day centre' as in the National Health Strategy (2001). This has meant that the heterogeneity of the older population has not been fully acknowledged and other day services that might be more appropriate to a variety of needs have not been developed.

In addition, the objectives of day services for older people have hitherto been quite limited and appear to be based on low expectations for the client group. In some cases, this appears to have encouraged the development of minimum services that assume older people are passive recipients of care and unable to benefit from activation and stimulation. Whether these service objectives truly reflect the needs of older people and their carers is unclear, as they have rarely been consulted in this regard. This highlights the need for day service planning to include provision for consultation with older people and their carers.

On the basis of discussions with older people, carers and service providers, the Council recommends that the service objectives proposed in policy documents are still wholly relevant and applicable, but must be re-prioritised to respond effectively to the needs of all client groups, including carers, in the various types of day facility. This is particularly important when the client group is of a more dependent nature. In dementia-specific day centres and day care centres, for example, respite for carers is vitally important due to the strain that a high level of constant caring places upon them. Similarly, ongoing nursing and therapeutic support are more important in these centres than in a social club. The Council recommends that the service objectives for the different types of centre, as detailed in the report, be adopted regionally and nationally in policy documents concerning older people and that they be used as a basis on which services are developed.

Services Required to Meet Primary and Secondary Objectives

The lack of proper definitions regarding service objectives has resulted in a parallel lack of definition regarding the services that are required to meet those objectives. It has never been made clear, for instance, that professional staff (rather than voluntary) may be required in the centres in order to monitor health, provide therapy or promote self-development. Similarly, the fact that resources are required to provide adequate facilities within which such objectives can be achieved, has never been highlighted. This report provides details of the essential services required in each of the different types of facility. The Council recommends that day services be fully resourced to provide the services necessary to achieve their primary and secondary objectives.

Evaluation of Services

The research demonstrated that sometimes the critical issue was not whether a particular service was available but whether a quality service was being provided.

It has been noted that evaluation of day services has, to date, been piecemeal and that there is no evidence of a clear set of criteria being used to evaluate day services for the elderly in the Irish context (Convery, 1987). The Council believes that this report will assist service planners and providers in conducting evaluations and delivering quality services by outlining the components required to fulfil service objectives. The Council recommends that these components be used as the basis for evaluations of the different facilities.

The National Health Strategy (2001) has stated that monitoring and evaluation must become intrinsic to the approach taken at all levels of the health services, and that there is a need for a more focused and in-depth assessment of the quality, equity and person-centredness of particular services through formal evaluations. It is envisaged that the Department of Health and Children will require each health board to specify the services for which formal evaluations will be undertaken by their respective monitoring and evaluation units. The Council recommends that health boards, with a view to determining standards and principles of good practice, should evaluate day services. Evaluations should be used as a basis for the continuing development of these services.

The Council recommends that a crucial component of the evaluation process should be consultation with users of day services and their carers, because day service objectives are predominantly related to how well the services meet the needs of these groups. Consultation with service users is not a new phenomenon and many service providers stipulate the inclusion of the service user perspective in evaluation exercises. However, Bauld *et al.* (2000) noted that older people tend to be less critical of services and service providers, and usually have lower expectations of what services can provide. This is consistent with the findings of this study, which demonstrated that the majority of older people tended not to give negative feedback about services. This contrasts with the views of service providers, who noted difficulties and adverse factors that they felt directly affected the quality of service received by older people. Bauld *et al.* (2000) recommended strategies for eliciting more critical views from older people and the Council recommends that health boards adopt these when conducting evaluations of day services. These include:

- combining global satisfaction measures with specific service measures

- assessing satisfaction over time rather than once off

- assessing satisfaction in conjunction with other indicators, such as changes in physical and mental health

- using multivariate techniques to analyse any response bias

- using mixed methods (surveys, focus groups, in-depth interviewing) in the study design.

The Council further recommends that a complaints mechanism should be firmly established within each day facility and that staff and service users, including carers, should be made aware of it. In addition, there should be clear signposts with regard to the effective communication of complaints and grievances. The Council welcomes the establishment of a complaints mechanism in each of the health boards and recommends that day services established by statutory, voluntary and private organisations be made aware of their rights and responsibilities in this regard.

Structural and Process Components of Service Delivery Required to Achieve Service Objectives

The service providers, in particular, highlighted issues that currently act as barriers to the achievement of the service objectives of different centres.

1. Funding

Funding of day services in Ireland has, historically, been discretionary because health boards have no statutory obligation to support community services. The voluntary sector is one of the largest providers of day services for older people and its involvement in the planned development of these services is crucial. However, lack of clarity regarding the funding relationships between health boards and voluntary organisations has had direct negative implications for the level and quality of services provided in the centres. As a result, the expertise of the voluntary sector is not fully realised (O'Shea and O'Reilly, 1999).

Funding arrangements between health boards and voluntary bodies are often *ad hoc* in nature and this makes planning difficult. Without guaranteed funding linked to service level agreements, it is very difficult for voluntary groups to provide services in a structured and consistent manner. Consistent funding arrangements for voluntary providers and the setting of targets for service delivery, based on an accurate assessment of local needs, would lead to a more efficient use of scarce voluntary resources (O'Shea and O'Reilly, 1999).

The Years Ahead (1988) recommended that service agreements be drawn up between health boards and the voluntary agencies providing day services. Therefore, the Council welcomes the commitments made in the National Health Strategy that 'service agreements between the health boards and the voluntary sector will be extended to all service providers and associated performance indicators will be introduced' (*Quality and Fairness*, 2001). The Council reiterates and develops a number of the recommendations it has made in the past with regard to the relationship between voluntary day service providers and the health boards (see Convery, 1987). These are:

- that standardised grant application procedures for voluntary organisations wishing to set up day services should be established with clearly defined criteria for grant eligibility

- that service level agreements should govern funding arrangements between health boards and service providers and should, at a minimum, cover the following:

  - stated service objectives

  - evidence of needs assessment having been carried out

- number and type of staff to be employed

- quantum and type of services to be offered

- breakdown of costs

- number of clients to receive the service

- amount of funding to be allocated with funding dates/intervals specified.

- that there should be a standardised approach within health boards to charging day service users

- that funding levels to service providers should be adequate to cover the following:

  - payment to day service supervisors and staff as appropriate

  - staff recruitment and training

  - recruitment, training and support of volunteers

  - transport costs

  - provision and maintenance of minimum standard buildings and facilities

  - insurance cover

  - provision of nutritious meals and snacks

  - the cost of providing therapeutic services including chiropody, physiotherapy, speech and language therapy, and occupational therapy as needed

  - provision of a range of social activities reflecting the preferences of the clientele.

Finally, the Council would like to signal its concern that services for older people are especially vulnerable in times when public funds are being rationed. There is a direct relationship between lack of community supports for older people and their placement in long-term care. The Council proposes that funding of day services will enable more people to remain in the community (which is consistent with government policy objectives) and may reduce instances of expensive and inappropriate institutionalisation. In addition, older people in acute hospitals may find it easier to return to their own homes if community supports, such as day care, are made more available.

2. Staffing

The Council recommends that staff ratios in day service facilities be increased so that stated service objectives may be achieved. It also recommends that further research be carried out to establish norms and standards for staffing levels in day services for older people. The establishment of these norms will have direct implications regarding the resources that should be allocated to the different facilities in order to provide a quality service.

Depending on the type of centre in question, a specific complement of trained staff is required to ensure that the service objectives of the centre are being achieved. The research has highlighted staffing difficulties at all levels. The lack of availability of qualified physiotherapists and chiropodists was identified as a critical deficit. The Bacon report (2001) recommended initiatives regarding the financing, training and regulation of the supply of qualified therapeutic staff to meet current serious service deficits. The Council endorses these recommendations and urges that they be acted upon in the short- to medium-term to alleviate the current shortages.

The Council has previously recommended that chiropody services be expanded significantly on both a community and domiciliary basis (HeSSOP, 2001, p51). However, the Council recognises that there are a number of issues affecting the availability of chiropodists in day services. Chiropody services are free to medical card holders but there are issues surrounding payment structures, particularly within a day care or residential setting (group payment structures), that act as a deterrent to chiropodists working in the health services.

The Council urges immediate action to remedy increasing problems regarding the availability of chiropody services in day service settings. In order to increase the number of chiropodists eligible to work for the health boards, the Council recommends that negotiations with organisations representing chiropodists be given priority, to resolve current difficulties regarding registration of chiropodists in Ireland. The Council also recommends that current fee levels and payment structures be conducive to attracting and retaining chiropodists in public service.

The Council further recommends that in the short-term, where the provision of these therapeutic services in the centres themselves is not possible, day service providers be funded to employ chiropodists on a sessional basis and that there also be adequate referral mechanisms to such services outside the centres. The Council welcomes the *Primary Care Strategy* (2001) in this regard. The Council is hopeful that there will be more access to these professional services both in and outside the centres, given that a team of professionals will support a specific geographical area. Therefore, the Council urges the Primary Care Task Force to strongly consider the future relationship between Primary Care Teams and day services in its current programme of work.

The research also highlighted staff shortages in other areas. It was noted, for example, that a lack of care attendants and volunteers meant that some service providers were under increasing strain just to provide a minimum service for the older people attending the centres. The development of the social economy as a means of improving the level of service provision required to meet the needs of older people in the community is one solution to a situation where demand for services is not met. Community, voluntary and volunteer service provision becomes even more important when public resources are constrained. The National Health Strategy (2001) has stated that 'community groups will be funded to facilitate volunteers in providing support services such as shopping, visiting and transport for older people' and that measures will be introduced to 'foster volunteerism' in the community, particularly with regard to providing services for older people. However, the Strategy did not make any suggestions regarding how these measures would be put into operation. The Council recommends that explicit measures be developed and funded to encourage the wider public to volunteer their services in day facilities for older people. The contribution of volunteers must be acknowledged and investment made in recruiting, training and supporting them. One option is for health boards to fund volunteer bureaux that could provide volunteers for a variety of settings in any one area or region. While the Council acknowledges the importance and potential of the social economy in providing community services for older people, including day services, it recommends that the primary responsibility for ensuring the availability of needed services remain with the health boards.

Concern was also expressed that FÁS and Community Employment (CE) schemes, which provide staff for the centres, are constantly under threat of termination. The numbers on these schemes have been gradually reduced since 1999 when the numbers were close to 40,000. It is expected that the average number of participants on these schemes will be 22,000 in 2003 although this number may be further reduced if the mainstreaming of CE services proceeds as planned (Comhairle, 2003).

The Council is concerned that health and social services for older people have not been accorded priority status by the Department of Enterprise, Trade and Employment (DETE) and FÁS in the face of impending reductions in numbers.

If FÁS and CE schemes are to be cut back or eliminated (as has been threatened), the Council recommends that the health boards compensate day service providers adequately so that they can source their own staff.

Training of staff at all levels is critical to ensuring that a quality service is delivered and that older people's health and social gains can be assured. The Council recommends that day service staff be provided with opportunities for continuing personal and professional development, and that volunteers receive training and support that is funded by the health boards. It believes that training should provide staff with the skills necessary to provide care for older people, as well as to motivate and activate them.

3. Transport

This report confirms previous findings (Convery, 1987) that transport is crucial to facilitating access to day services. Funding is necessary for centres to make adequate transport arrangements. The research has indicated that transport that is owned or controlled by the centres is required to enable older people to access the services they need and the Council recommends that dedicated funding be allocated to this end.

The Council welcomes the Inter-Departmental Committee on Rural Transport that is at present considering issues relating to the availability of transport services in rural areas. It reiterates a recommendation in the HeSSOP (2001) report that

County Development Boards examine and promote transport accessibility for older people at a county level. It also supports the recommendation by the Equality Authority for a review of transport schemes to be carried out by the Department of Social and Family Affairs in order to guarantee a comprehensive package of transport and other services is devised for older people in the community (Equality Authority, 2002).

4. Activities Programmes and the Social Model of Care

There are a number of important issues to consider with regard to activities programmes in day services. The variety of activities on offer is directly linked to funding, as funding determines whether centres have sufficient staff to initiate and engage in social activities programmes with the older people, and whether a centre has appropriate facilities, equipment and space to host them.

Consultations during the preparation of the report highlighted the importance of providing a choice of activities for older people. However, the preferences expressed by the older people for less active pursuits, such as sitting and chatting or playing bingo, may have been based on the services currently available to them rather than a range of possible activities that could be provided in centres. Therefore, the Council recommends that older people be provided with a real and meaningful choice of activities. It has been noted in the past that 'ageist assumptions have coloured the way in which client needs have been defined and have influenced the way in which programmes have been developed and services delivered' (Convery, 1987). This did not apply to all centres, where the lack of provision of stimulating activities could be related to funding constraints as opposed to stereotypical negative expectations of older people.

Where this does apply the result is that, at best, older people accept the ageist assumptions that are associated with the sedentary activities provided by some of the centres and, at worst, they may internalise these assumptions and develop ageist attitudes about themselves and their own levels of activity. In addition, evidence from the older people who did not attend the centres indicated that there was a perception among them that it was only the less active, more dependent and lonely older people who would benefit from attending the centres. It appears that unimaginative programmes of activity may have contributed to a certain level of stigma being attached to attending day services that acts as a barrier to some older people attending.

The social club that was visited during the fieldwork for this report presents a good example of the range of activities that can be provided in a day service for older people. The club was also involved in various initiatives with the wider community, thus encouraging both intercommunity and intergenerational solidarity. While it is acknowledged that some activities will not appeal to all, the provision of choice is critical in raising older people's expectations regarding what they can achieve, and in raising the profile of the centres within the wider community.

The crucial difference between the social club and the other centres examined for this report was that the emphasis in the social club was more on the personal, emotional and spiritual development of the older person (although this also applies to some of the social club/day centres and day care centres that were visited). In many facilities the lack of funding and staff, despite service providers' best intentions, often conspired to prevent adequate emphasis being placed on the social development of the older person. In a social model of care the priority is to incorporate and/or develop the social life of individuals. Its overriding principle is an emphasis on respecting individual differences and promoting individual choices. The underlying philosophy is that people never outgrow the capacity to learn and to experience. The Council supports Convery's recommendation (1987) that day services for older people adopt a social model (rather than a medical service model more appropriate to day hospital services) with emphasis placed on activation, socialisation and maximisation of older people's functional ability. Services should reflect their interests and abilities, and capitalise on their life experiences.

The Council recommends that service providers consult with older people about their preferences regarding the services and activities they would like to avail of in day service settings. This is consistent with commitments made in the National Health Strategy which has stated that, in order to ensure that appropriate care is delivered in the appropriate setting, 'health care workers will be encouraged and facilitated to accommodate, as appropriate, the wishes of individual patients/clients' (*Quality and Fairness*, 2001, p79). The Council further recommends that older men in particular be targeted and consulted with regard to their service preferences and their ideas about what a day service might ideally offer them.

5. Carers' Needs

Consistent with the responses from the older people who were interviewed, the carers also expressed high levels of satisfaction with the services being offered to their loved ones in the various facilities. However, the service providers, particularly in the more care-oriented centres, felt that the opening hours did not facilitate carers who wished or needed to work outside the home. In addition, the providers proposed that the centres should be open at weekends to provide carers with more respite from caring than they currently receive. The Council recommends that day services be funded adequately to enable them to open for a sufficient time each day to accommodate the carers most in need of services. Increased resourcing of day services should be accompanied by increased funding of other respite services, including home sitting, weekend and intermittent respite services, to alleviate the burden on carers.

6. Partnership

Day services should not operate in isolation from other elements in the continuum of community care services. In the current climate of tightening resources it is sensible to make better use of existing resources before making demands for an allocation of new resources. The Council recommends that day services be linked to all relevant providers of services to older people and that they work together in partnership to meet the needs of older people in the community in an integrated and co-ordinated fashion. These relevant providers include physiotherapists, chiropodists, occupational therapists, ophthalmologists, dieticians, social workers and pharmacists to name but a few. These links are critical to ensuring that pathways to care and opportunity can be identified and developed for all members in the centres.

Within day services, the Council recommends that a partnership approach be adopted, between staff and older people who use the service, so that people attending centres are enabled to become partners in their own care, as recommended in *Quality and Fairness* (2001). The adoption of an ethos of partnership within the centres would remove the traditional emphasis on the custodial aspects of care and enable members to influence how services are planned and provided. A prerequisite for this partnership approach is consultation with older people themselves. They should be facilitated to both assist in providing services themselves and not to be passive recipients of care. In order to ensure that appropriate care is delivered in the appropriate setting, the Council recommends that older people be empowered to play a major role in shaping the services that they receive. It is interesting to note that many of the older people attending the centres referred to the numerous services that are provided at a personal level. It could be said that in a number of cases, the service providers are acting as advocates for the older people by helping them to conduct business with, for example, banks, doctors and solicitors. In this context, the Council recommends that advocacy for individual older people and older people as a group, should be central to the work of day service staff.

The Council also recommends that the potential for promoting the health and autonomy of older people in a day service environment be realised by providing them with the information necessary to enable them to become partners in their own care, to make informed choices and to access services and activities appropriate to their needs and preferences. *The Years Ahead Report: A Review of the Implementation of its Recommendations* (1997) noted that day centres were good places to offer structured health education programmes which would empower older people, prolonging their period of independent and active ageing, and encouraging their full and active participation in society. The Council reiterates its support for the Action Plan on the information needs of older people (Ruddle *et al.*, 2002), to ensure that they receive and understand the information required to access the services they need to help them continue living at home.

With a large proportion of day services being provided by the voluntary sector, it is crucial that a partnership approach be adopted between the statutory and voluntary sectors to ensure that all available resources in the community are optimally utilised. The extension of service agreements between the health boards and the voluntary sector, as proposed in the National Health Strategy (2001), will facilitate the adoption of this partnership approach. The Council recommends that a partnership approach be adopted between the health boards and the voluntary and private sectors to develop and support day services. The employment of community workers to foster positive relationships between the health boards and service providers, as in the Southern Health Board, is one option; the development of voluntary support units within health boards is another. It makes sense for health boards to support the development of day service networks and to define standardised policies and procedures that apply to all service providers within an area or health board region.

Representation by voluntary organisations on the health boards tends to vary and the Council feels that this sector will continue to have little influence on management decision making if it is not represented fully at a regional level. The Council recommends that health boards signal their commitment to better partnership by encouraging representation of voluntary organisations on health boards, particularly organisations representing older people. Legislation regarding the composition of health boards may need to be amended in light of this recommendation. Furthermore, the Council welcomes the guidelines (*Community Participation Guidelines*, 2002) developed on the basis of commitments made in the National Health Strategy (2001) that 'a provision will be made for the participation of the community in decisions about the delivery of health and personal social services'. The Council hopes that these guidelines will enable the development of a culture of participation and partnership between voluntary organisations and health boards and between the health boards and the wider community.

Consultations during the preparation of this report also highlighted the need for a liaison officer from the statutory sector to work with and to encourage voluntary organisations in the provision of services for older people. Voluntary organisations often find it difficult to find relevant and up-to-date information about regulations with which they have to comply in providing their services. A liaison officer could provide information as required and act as a link between statutory and voluntary organisations. The Council notes that a model for this type of service exists in the North Eastern Health Board. In Cavan/Monaghan, a project manager post with specific responsibility for day care services was established three years ago.

If one of the roles of day services is to provide relief from caring, then carers must be allowed to contribute to the process of identifying care pathways for their loved ones. This is particularly important given that a number of carers are in fact older people themselves, and that their changing needs and requirements must be identified and accommodated. Therefore, the Council recommends that day services liaise closely with carers to identify their specific and changing needs, as well as those of the older people for whom they are caring. Caring for older people can be a source of strain, as well as psychological and emotional distress (O'Shea and O'Reilly, 1999). In many cases, the care-giving role can have a negative effect on social and family life, with the emotional and social effects being detrimental to physical health especially.

A combination of such pressures may occasionally contribute to situations of elder abuse. In addition, social isolation may increase older people's vulnerability to potential abuse. The Council recommends that all health and social service providers, including day service staff, become aware of both the signs of elder abuse and the appropriate responses to suspected abuse. Structures should be developed by each health board to include service providers in training programmes so that they can equip staff with the necessary information and skills, as recommended in *Protecting Our Future* (2002).

Partnership between day services and the wider community is also critical for the future development of these services. The Council recommends that, in the current climate of fiscal constraints, the most pragmatic approach to partnership is to conduct an audit of relevant services already available in the community, with a view to investigating how they can be combined or consolidated in order to increase provision, for example, school buses which are usually used in the morning and afternoon could also be used to take older people to and from day centres.

Service providers within the community should also be encouraged to advertise and provide their services, wherever possible, within centres. This may have the effect of extending choice with regard to the programme of activities that could be offered in centres. This in turn may also contribute to a positive image of ageing within the wider community and, indeed, among older people and service providers themselves.

Support for those Older People Who Do Not Wish or Cannot Attend Day Services

It is the expressed wish of older people themselves to remain living in their own homes for as long as possible. It is therefore reasonable to assume that a significant number of them may have no interest in attending day services that are available outside their homes. During the research, it was noted that some older people are reluctant to attend.

As noted earlier, men in particular are difficult to attract to the centres. Dissatisfaction with the activities on offer was cited as one of the main reasons for not attending. This is consistent with recent research (Economic and Social Research Council, 2003) that showed that statutory and voluntary organisations providing social facilities were presently equipped for the needs of lone widows, since most husbands predecease their wives. It concluded that concerted efforts needed to be made to make clubs aimed at older people more congenial for older men.

The benefits of day services as a forum for health promotion and indeed, for health monitoring have been confirmed by the service providers who took part in the research and in consultations during the preparation of the report. A dilemma arises if older men cannot be encouraged to attend. The Council proposes that activities programmes must be restructured away from ones that are female-based to ones that achieve a greater gender balance. However, it must also be acknowledged that, for some men, this reorientation of activities may be insufficient to attract their attendance. This highlights the necessity to re-think how men will be encouraged to become active participants in their own care.

The recent Health Strategy (2001) has highlighted men's health as an area that requires increased attention. As recommended earlier, consultations with older men themselves will be crucial in this regard. It is only by asking older men what services they want and how they want them to be provided will their needs and preferences be accommodated and their health status improved.

In addition, consultations during the preparation of this report also highlighted that dementia-specific day centres were not always appropriate for some older people who would prefer to remain in their own homes and who would become quite distressed if removed from their familiar environments. Finally, for the incapacitated and housebound, attendance at day services provided in the community may not be an option, even when suitable transport is provided. For these people, the provision of home help and home sitting services is usually a more appropriate option.

The Council recommends, therefore, that other community services be developed for older people who do not wish to attend day services in local centres. Such services should be available to meet their health and social needs, and should reflect their preferences. It further proposes that, with current service provision at such a low level, a large sustained investment in domiciliary community care services such as home help, home support, meals-on-wheels, nursing, occupational therapy, physiotherapy and social work is necessary. The Council again recommends that these services be designated as core services, available to older people by right.

Bacon, P., 2001. *Current and Future Supply and Demand Conditions in the Labour Market for Certain Professional Therapists*. Dublin: Stationery Office.

Bauld, L., Chesterman, J. and Judge, K., 2000. 'Measuring Satisfaction with Social Care Amongst Older Service Users: Issues from the Literature' *Health and Social Care in the Community*, Vol. 8(5): 316-324.

Comhairle, 2003. *Relate: Information for All*. March, Vol. 30(6). Dublin: Comhairle.

Convery, J., 1987. *Choices in Community Care: Day Centres for the Elderly in the Eastern Health Board*. Dublin: National Council for the Aged.

Department of Health and Children, 2001. *Quality and Fairness: A Health System for You*. Dublin: Stationery Office.

Department of Health and Children, 2001. *Primary Care: A New Direction*. Dublin: Stationery Office.

Department of Health and Children, 2002. *Community Participation Guidelines*. Dublin: Stationery Office.

Department of Health, 1988. *The Years Ahead: A Policy for the Elderly*. Dublin: Stationery Office.

Equality Authority, 2002. *Implementing Equality for Older People*. Dublin: Equality Authority.

Economic and Social Research Council, 2003. *Research Findings: 12 From the Growing Older Programme*. Sheffield: ESRC Growing Older Programme.

Garavan, R., Winder, R. and McGee, H., 2001. *Health and Social Services for Older People (HeSSOP)*. Dublin: National Council on Ageing and Older People.

National Working Group on Performance Indicators, 2002. *Glossary of Terms: Services for Older Persons*. Dublin: Stationery Office.

North Eastern Health Board, 2001. *Healthy Ageing: A Secure Future. A Five Year Strategy for the Delivery of Services to Older People*. North Eastern Health Board.

O'Shea, E. and O'Reilly, S., 1999. *An Action Plan for Dementia*. Dublin: National Council on Ageing and Older People.

Report of the Working Group on Elder Abuse, 2002. *Protecting Our Future*. Dublin: Stationery Office.

Ruddle, H., Donoghue, F. and Mulvihill, R., 1997. *The Years Ahead Report: A Review of the Implementation of its Recommendations*. Dublin: National Council on Ageing and Older People.

Ruddle, H., Prizeman, G., Haslett, D., Mulvihill, R. and Kelly, E., 2002. *Meeting the Health, Social Care and Welfare Services Information Needs of Older People*. Dublin: National Council on Ageing and Older People.

28

Executive Summary

Executive Summary

Background to the Study

In 1987, the Convery report *Choices in Community Care: Day Centres for the Elderly in the Eastern Health Board* noted that a weakness in the community care system as a whole had been that service objectives, including those for day services for older people, had not been adequately developed. A year later in 1988, *The Years Ahead* report defined the main purposes of day centres but did not develop service objectives in such a way as to give meaningful direction to service operations and development.

There are several reasons contributing to the lack of development of service objectives for day services for older people. One of these is undoubtedly the historical confusion surrounding the terminology used to describe very different types of day service (leading to older people being directed to facilities that may not be appropriate to their needs). A second reason is the lack of consultation with older people who use day facilities and their carers, those older people in the community who do not use or want to use the facilities, and those who work in them or refer older people to them.

In order to progress the development of day service objectives and to establish a continuum of day facilities appropriate to older people's diverse needs, abilities and preferences, the National Council on Ageing and Older People commissioned a report to:

- identify the main models of day facilities that exist 'on the ground'

- consult with older people, their carers and service providers in order to revise and develop primary and secondary objectives for each of the models identified

- define the components of service delivery to assist in evaluating how well the different models of day service provision meet these objectives.

Focus of the Study

The focus of the study was on day services as an ongoing social support, rather than as short-term rehabilitation, support or protective supervision for older people. Therefore, the parameters of study exclude day services, such as day hospitals and psychiatric day hospitals where duration of attendance is intended to be short-term, and are confined to those categories where attendance is expected to be ongoing and indefinite.

Aims of the Study

The aims of the study were to:

- develop service objectives and identify the components of service delivery required to achieve those objectives for each type of facility under investigation

- propose appropriate evaluation processes which will allow the facilities to be evaluated (following the development of service objectives and the components of service delivery required to achieve those objectives)

- formulate recommendations relevant to health and social care policy with regard to the future development of day services in Ireland.

In order to achieve these aims:

- a Preliminary Classification of Day Services in Ireland was developed that provided details of four day service models identified by the Consultative Committee as being in existence 'on the ground'. These models were day care centres, day centres, social clubs and dementia-specific day centres

- consultations were carried out with older people attending these day facilities, older people in the same communities not attending, family carers of older people, service providers working in these facilities and Public Health Nurses (PHNs)

- a Revised Classification of Day Services in Ireland was then drawn up that included revised models, as well as primary and secondary service objectives. The revised models are day care centres, social club/day centres, social clubs and dementia-specific day centres

- detailed service delivery components for the different models were presented, as were guidelines for evaluating how well the services achieved their objectives.

Methods

The expertise of the Consultative Committee was used to identify fifteen day facilities throughout the country which were felt to be representative of the different types of day services detailed in the Preliminary Classification of Day Services in Ireland. Consultations were carried out with 78 older people attending these centres, 47 service providers who managed and staffed the centres, 20 family carers, 14 PHNs and 23 older people in the community not attending a day centre.

Outcomes

Older people and their carers, service providers and PHNs, clearly valued day services and recognised their importance in helping older people to remain in their own homes in dignity and independence. As a result of comprehensive consultations with all the parties involved, revised primary and secondary objectives were established for each model. The primary objectives for each model were as follows.

Day care centres

- to prevent older people from going into long-term care

- to support independent living among older people

- to provide assistance with personal care and health care

- to facilitate activation/social interaction

- to provide support and respite for carers

- to provide a forum for health promotion.

Social club/day centres

- to prevent older people from going into long-term care

- to facilitate social interaction/social activities

- to encourage personal development

- to provide a forum for health promotion.

Social clubs

- to prevent older people from going into long-term care

- to facilitate social interaction/social activities

- to facilitate personal development

- to facilitate empowerment

- to encourage integration into the community

- to provide a forum for health promotion.

Dementia-specific day centres

- to prevent older people from going into long-term care

- to provide protective and appropriate supervision for older people with dementia

- to provide assistance with personal care and health care

- to provide support and respite for carers

- to provide a forum for health promotion.

Defining the Components of Service Delivery in Order to Evaluate How Well a Service is Achieving its Objectives

Components of service delivery were defined, using the classic Donabedian (1966; 1988) structure, process and outcome model, in order to instruct the evaluation of a service and how well it is meeting its objectives.

The structural components of service delivery considered were:

- funding and its level of security

- staffing requirements needed in order to meet the varying health care, social care and dependency needs of older people attending the various facilities

- level of service provision

- services provided.

The process aspects considered were:

- the ethos, values and principles that direct and inform the service

- the process of care delivery

- involvement of older people and their carers.

Having presented the structural and process components of service delivery required to achieve the service objectives in each of the four models of day services, various evaluation models were discussed, including descriptive evaluation, programme review evaluation and impact evaluation. Other questions considered included the need to prioritise the components of service delivery to be evaluated, the methodologies that could be used in conducting evaluations and recommendations as to who should conduct the evaluations.

Challenges to the Future Development of Day Services for Older People in Ireland

The consultations also highlighted a number of challenges to the future development of day facilities for older people.

Many of these challenges have already been very well documented and are not unknown. Many of the deficits discussed in this study in relation to dementia-specific day centres have already been analysed in the O'Shea and O'Reilly (1999) report, *An Action Plan for Dementia*. The considerable difficulties in providing older people in day care centres with the appropriate and requisite care have been argued in the Bacon (2001) report, *Current and Future Supply and Demand Conditions in the Labour Market for Certain Professional Therapists*.

In spite of these challenges, and they are many, this study clearly demonstrates that older people want to remain at home and in their communities for as long as possible. A spectrum of quality services appropriate to their varying needs, abilities and preferences, must be available to them so that they can live out their older years with confidence, dignity, enjoyment and respect.

35

References

Bacon, P., 2001. *Current and Future Supply and Demand Conditions in the Labour Market for Certain Professional Therapists.* Dublin: Stationery Office.

Convery, J., 1987. *Choices in Community Care: Day Centres for the Elderly in the Eastern Health Board.* Dublin: National Council for the Aged.

Department of Health, 1988. *The Years Ahead: A Policy for the Elderly.* Dublin: Stationery Office.

O'Shea, E. and O'Reilly, S., 1999. *An Action Plan for Dementia.* Dublin: National Council on Ageing and Older People.

Chapter One

Introduction
to the Study

Chapter One

Introduction to the Study

1.1 Background to the Study

One of the key achievements of the last century has been the improvement in average life expectancy. Consistent with other European nations, Irish society is ageing. In the mid-1990s, 11 per cent of the population was aged over 65 years. By 2030, this figure will rise to around twenty per cent of the population. In real terms, the number of people aged over 65 years is predicted to more than double during this 35-year period: from 402,000 to around 847,000 (*Quality and Fairness: A Health System for You*, Department of Health and Children, 2001). This growth will continue to give rise to additional demands for services for older people.

The broad aim of health and social service provision for older people in Ireland is to maintain them in dignity and independence in their own homes for as long as possible or practicable (*The Years Ahead*, 1988; *Shaping a Healthier Future*, 1994; *Adding Years to Life*, 1996; *The Years Ahead Report: A Review of the Implementation of its Recommendations*, 1997; *Quality and Fairness*, 2001). In order to realise this aim, a continuum of care is needed. The services that constitute this continuum include home help, meals and laundry services, nursing, medical, paramedical and respite services, home maintenance and, most importantly, day services.

Day services are provided by both statutory and voluntary agencies, frequently working in partnership, and are an essential element in the continuum of services needed to maintain older people at home. They provide support, social contact, assistance and relief to carers, and can reduce unnecessary admission to institutional care.

The central role of day services has been repeatedly recognised, most recently in the Health Strategy *Quality and Fairness* (Department of Health and Children, 2001), which committed to creating 7,000 additional day centre places with a promise to recruit a multi-disciplinary range of staff to support the development of primary care services, including day care services. This has been endorsed in *Implementing Equality for Older People* (Equality Authority, 2002).

Older people are a heterogeneous group and their physical health status, emotional and psychological needs, and interests and abilities vary greatly. By determining what types of day service older people use or want, as well as what they, their carers and their service providers expect from such services, the development of the range of services required can be facilitated.

1.2 Supported Home Care for Older People

The authors of the HeSSOP study (Garavan *et al.*, 2001) emphasised that supported home care, of which day care is a part, is the most underdeveloped component of care for older people in our health and social service system. In spite of the fact that the broad aim of social service provision is to maintain older people in independence in their own homes for as long as possible, long-stay nursing facilities have more often been targeted by policy-makers as a main area for development (Convery, 2001a).

Convery noted that the current system whereby older people are entitled to apply for financial assistance towards the cost of nursing home care but not for non-institutional care, results in a bias towards institutional care, despite health policy favouring home and community care. There is no statutory entitlement to either assessment of social care needs or financial assistance to pay for social care services, which would support older people in maintaining their independence. The development and allocation of social care services is discretionary. Health boards, therefore, are not obliged to provide social care services and older people have no right to expect them, even when they have been assessed as being in need of them.

Funding and its level of security, has direct implications for the level and standard of service provided in all types of day facility for older people. In 1999, the National Council on Ageing and Older People in the report *Income, Deprivation* and *Well-Being Among Older Irish People* (Layte *et al.*, 1999), recommended that the provision of core services such as day care, should be underpinned by legislation and statutory funding.

Prior to the Layte *et al.* (1999) report, the Council made recommendations regarding funding procedures for day (care) centres both in Convery (1987) and in Ruddle *et al.* (1997). The Convery recommendations included criteria for statutory funding commitments and levels to voluntary organisations, funding for staffing, transport and a minimum level of service. Ruddle *et al.* (1997) reiterated many of the earlier funding recommendations and also included a strong recommendation that health boards be obliged in legislation to provide day services of a specified quality with a comprehensive range of services to all older people who require them.

A critical weakness in the community care system as a whole has been that social services have never been established on an equitable basis. The Health Strategy *Shaping a Healthier Future* (Department of Health, 1994) acknowledged that this was because there were a number of services for which no eligibility criteria, or rules governing charges, had been established in legislation.

Although the level of investment in services for older people began to increase from a very low base in the late 1990s, it is still the case, as pointed out in *Quality and Fairness* (Department of Health and Children, 2001), that gaps in service provision remain in several community support services including day care. This most recent Health Strategy, through its four national goals of *better health for everyone, fair access, responsiveness and appropriate care delivery and high performance*, emphasised the need for increased support for community care services for older people, including day care.

In the context of the issues raised in the Ombudsman's report on the Nursing Home Subvention Scheme (2001), the Health Strategy argues that community support services are both more appropriate and preferable to older people and their families. The Health Strategy undertook to amend the Nursing Home Subvention Scheme to take account of the Ombudsman's report. It recognised that a large number of older people would like the option of receiving care in their own homes rather than in a nursing home. It also proposed reform of the existing schemes in order to introduce an integrated care subvention scheme that maximises support for home care.

There is a dearth of research in Ireland on day services for older people. It is 16 years since the Convery report (1987) was prepared for the National Council of the Aged, (now the NCAOP).

In 1988 *The Years Ahead* report, following on from the Convery report, made a number of recommendations on day care, including:

- that health boards be obliged by law to provide or support day care centres for the elderly, including transport to and from such centres

- that the Department of Health provide guidelines for the operation and management of day centres

- that a model contract be drawn up by the Department of Health for use by health boards and voluntary bodies where voluntary organisations provide a day service on behalf of a health board

- that where voluntary organisations are providing day care services, health boards provide opportunities for staff to develop their expertise

- that in each of the next five years, a total of £0.5m (€635,000) be allocated by the Department of Health for the purpose of establishing day centres.

Almost a decade later when *The Years Ahead* (Ruddle *et al.*, 1997) report was reviewed, none of these recommendations had been implemented, leading the National Council on Ageing and Older People to conclude:

'Day care is probably the most neglected part of the community care sector. Day centres seem to be low on the priority list of health authorities and are provided on a discretionary basis.'

There have been improvements since 1997 and there is evidence of an increased recognition of the benefit of day care for older people in Ireland. At a regional level the majority of health boards, in their strategic and service plans for older people, have developed and are continuing to develop services that enable older people to live with dignity and independence in their own homes.

However, as Convery (2001a) points out, there is still a very low support service base in Ireland with gaps in the availability of many services including day care. It argues that the provision of appropriate services for older people is affected by a multitude of factors, which have resulted in low coverage and variations in service provision within and between health board areas, as confirmed in the recent Eastern Regional Health Authority review (2001).

1.4 Issues of Definition

In addition to the problems of underfunding, statutory entitlement and eligibility, there are problems of definition. Over the years different models of day service provision have evolved including centres that are funded and managed by health boards, centres managed by voluntary organisations but funded by health boards, and centres where health boards and voluntary organisations work in partnership to both manage and fund them.

42

This has led to the inconsistencies articulated by Garavan *et al.* (2001) in the HeSSOP study:

> *'Because many of these day services were set up by different organisations, there is some inconsistency in terms of how these services are defined and what particular services are provided, for example, there are several services called 'day centres' that may be classified as 'day care units' because of the medical services offered there, while other 'day centres' offer purely social activities.'*

Although both Convery (1988) and Ruddle *et al.* (1997) used the terms 'day centre' and 'day care centre' interchangeably, there is a growing realisation of the need to define the differences between these facilities. The Eastern Health Board (now the Eastern Regional Health Authority) in its *Ten Year Action Plan for Services for Older Persons 1999-2008* (Eastern Health Board, 1998), differentiated between day centres/clubs and day care units for older people. It stated that the main objectives of day centres/clubs are as spelled out in *The Years Ahead* (1988).

These are to:

- provide a midday meal, a bath, laundry and hairdressing

- provide physiotherapy, occupational therapy and chiropody

- promote social contact and prevent loneliness

- relieve caring relatives

- provide social stimulation in a safe environment for older people.

Day care units, on the other hand, provide a service similar to that provided in a day hospital setting. In the view of the ERHA, they provide a full range of medical, nursing, paramedical and social services on a daily basis. These services reduce the need for admission to in-patient care, support the older person to remain at home and provide support to family carers.

The ERHA action plan emphasises the need for structured development of day centres/clubs for older persons in partnership with voluntary service providers. This is in order to meet the demands being made by an increasingly older population.

Even allowing for the fact that in their review of *The Years Ahead,* Ruddle *et al.* (1997) used the terms 'day centre' and 'day care centre' interchangeably, the authors had the greatest difficulty in simply estimating the number of centres provided, the number of places available, and the numbers of centres and places required in the future within each health board area.

Although *The Years Ahead* (1988), almost a decade earlier, had recommended ratios of one day care centre per 1,800 older people and one social club per 600 older people (using the Central Statistics Office's population projections for 2002 this would mean a total of 240 day care centres and 725 social clubs) the authors noted that many of the figures supplied were, in the majority of cases, approximations only. They concluded by saying:

> 'The fact that accurate information on the number of places was difficult to obtain, that there are wide variations in level of provision and that some areas have no day care facilities at all, highlights the need to designate day care facilities as a core service, whose provision is not discretionary but instead is provided to a certain standard throughout the country.'

In the *Review of the Implementation of the Ten Year Action Plan for Services for Older People 1999-2008* (ERHA, 2001), it is apparent that such difficulties still exist. While the ERHA estimates that there are currently approximately 2,000 day care places available in its region, it points out that in reality many of these 'places' are only available a couple of days a week. It confirms that the range of services provided varies from one day care centre to another. It also confirms that there is a serious deficit of day care services in parts of the region, with some areas having no services at all. The review concludes by stating:

> *'Appropriate day care support may provide a range of medical and social facilities to provide social interaction, respite facility for carers and ongoing maintenance and monitoring of health and functional level. The full range of day care models are required to provide the range of support required for older persons with varying degrees of dependency. These include: active retirement clubs, day centres, day care centres and day hospitals.'*

1.5 The Needs of Older People

Day services provide support, social contact, assistance and relief to carers, and can reduce unnecessary admission to institutional care. As with any social service provision, their successful delivery depends on being responsive to the needs of its clientele. *The Years Ahead* (1988) recognised this when it stated that day centres should not only provide support and social contact for older people living alone, but also assistance and relief to those caring for older relatives in the home. Tester (1996), in a study of day care provisions in Europe, detailed several of these needs:

- basic care e.g. meals, bathing, hair-care

- social contact e.g. companionship, social stimulation

- therapeutic activity e.g. keep fit, games, crafts

- emotional support e.g. coping with bereavement, coping with loneliness

- information e.g. local facilities and services available

- medical/paramedical services e.g. physiotherapy, chiropody

- support for carers.

When asked to describe the support they needed in order to remain in their own homes for as long as possible, older people included the following (MacDonald, 1999):

- food and company

- opportunities for social activities and outings

- information and advice from day care staff

- respite for their carers

- minor medical services, such as first aid for minor injuries.

1.6 Social Inclusion

Blackman *et al.* (2001), in a comparative study of social care and social exclusion of older people, found that although social inclusion is usually defined in terms of income and employment status, the organisation and delivery of social care services can create barriers to the social inclusion of older people. Convery (2001b) discussed these barriers, including lack of entitlement, over-dependence on family care, predominance of the medical model of care and problems with access to services.

Clark (2001) points out that although day care can provide a social focus for people who might otherwise be very isolated, most day care settings are rarely seen by members of the community at large unless they have a relative in attendance. It argues that the goal must be to develop day services that respond to the challenges of inclusiveness. In Clark's view they must become:

- more flexible in time e.g. available at the weekend

- more flexible in space i.e. day services for older people should not be limited to 'traditional' centres but delivered in a wide variety of community settings including shopping centres, health centres etc.

- more flexible in response to individual requirements i.e. the traditional day care framework must be more responsive to older people's needs and interests.

1.7 The Special Needs of Older People with Dementia

An important area of social inclusion concerns the special needs of older people with dementia. O'Shea and O'Reilly (1999) in *An Action Plan for Dementia* argued that, in general, the needs of people in the early stages of dementia can be catered for in a 'generic day centre'. As dementia progresses, attendance at a dementia-specific or dementia-focused day centre may be more appropriate.

Those with more complex dementia may require care in a day hospital. However, regardless of the type of day service an older person with dementia attends, it is vital that their needs as an individual, as a family member and as a person with dementia, are met by that service.

46

1.8 Listening to the Views of Older People

'It is the collective experience of those on the receiving end which reveals most clearly what the whole picture looks like and where the gaps are. A strategy which aims to meet the needs of a section of the population is most unlikely to achieve its intended outcome if it fails to involve those whose needs it seeks to address both in defining the problem and in seeking the most effective solutions.'

(Harding, 1997)

In recent years a number of UK studies have been carried out in consultation with older people regarding their care (Barnes, 1994; MacDonald, 1999; Raynes, 2001). However, very little is known about the views of older people in Ireland regarding day services. Recent reports that have consulted with older people about aspects of day care include HeSSOP (Garavan *et al.*, 2001). When asked to think about future services, the vast majority of respondents in the HeSSOP report expressed a very clear preference for care at home.

The review by Ruddle *et al.* (1997) of *The Years Ahead* report did consult with Co-ordinators of Services for the Elderly and District Liaison Nurses with regard to their perceptions of both the value of and deficits in day care services. However, the authors pointed out that this is but one perspective and argued that comprehensive evaluation, which includes the views of the older users themselves, is a research area that needs to be addressed.

Consultations with older people are currently being undertaken by all the health boards to improve their involvement in the planning and evaluation of services. It is important, however, to add a note of caution: Delaney *et al.* (2001) mentioned the difficulties many researchers encounter when measuring the views of older people; Pope and May (1993) showed that older people in particular are likely to express more satisfaction with their health care than other sections of the patient population; Owens and Batchelor (1996) concluded that attempts to elicit the opinions of older patients require greater use of qualitative research; and Bauld *et al.* (2000), found that older people were more likely to report higher levels of satisfaction than younger people. This expression of higher satisfaction may be a combination of older people's dependency on service providers, their lower expectations of what a service can provide or perhaps, their lack of knowledge of alternative services or acceptable standards.

Based on its findings, Bauld *et al.* suggested strategies for improving measurement of older service users' perspectives, including combining methods such as in-depth interviewing and focus groups with more structured surveys. They also recommended combining simple, global satisfaction measures with more complex service-specific measures.

1.9 The Development of Service Objectives for Day Services

Convery (1987) noted that service objectives in the community care system, including day services for older people, have not been adequately developed. *The Years Ahead* (1988) defined the main purposes of day centres but did not develop service objectives in such a way as to give meaningful direction to service operations and development. More recent analysts of day services for older people frequently point out that there is little evaluation evidence available on which to base opinions of the effectiveness of services because, without clear statements of the aims of the services, it is difficult to measure outcomes (Tester, 2001; Hunter and Watt, 2001). The Tester review concludes by saying:

> *'The rhetoric of community care states aims of promoting independence, social integration, participation and empowerment, which are implicit in the provision of day services as part of community care; yet there is little clear and explicit consideration of how these principles and values are to be put into practice by day services, the diverse aims of which include social care and company, rehabilitation and treatment, assessment and monitoring, and support for carers.'*

Most, if not all, of the health boards have begun to consider the development of service objectives at community care level. An example of such aspirations can be found in the Western Health Board's *Health and Well-being for Older People: A Strategy for 2001-2006* (Western Health Board, 2001). The WHB proposes:

- to evaluate the activities of day care centres in order to assess their benefits for users and to determine principles of best practice

- to increase the number of day care places provided by the Board on an incremental basis over the next five years

- to work in partnership with voluntary organisations to extend and develop day centres throughout the region with particular emphasis on rural and remote areas.

A working group set up by Kerry Community Services is examining operational policies for day care centres (*Day Care Centres: Operational Policies – Draft Report*, Kerry Community Services, 2002). The draft report looks in some detail at values and principles of services that are linked to service objectives. It argues, for example, that services should be person-centred to respect the uniqueness of each individual older person and offer real choice. The services should promote a positive image of ageing, encourage older people to maintain a sense of identity, dignity and independence, and should remain sensitive to the changing needs and preferences of older people and their family carers.

The Midland Health Board is in the process of reviewing its day care services. The review group envisages day care service in the future as a multipurpose centre responding to older people's range of defined needs, and integrating community and voluntary efforts in a complete package of care. Day care interventions will be part of a full continuum of care response to the needs of older people. The Board hopes that these quality interventions will be delivered by competent and well-motivated staff, in conformance with best practice protocols, and will:

- meet the physical needs of older people

- promote social contact and social capital formation, and so reduce the psychological effects of loneliness

- promote social stimulation in a safe environment

- provide respite to caring families.

1.10 Evaluating Services

In the late 1990s, a number of UK-based organisations for older people, including Age Concern, Help the Aged and the National Pensioners' Convention, participated in a major programme on outcomes in community care practice from the perspective of users and carers. Underlying values, partnership, quality issues and organisational culture were central concerns for these groups.

Nocon *et al.* (1997), in a review of this programme, outlined four questions central to the process of service evaluation and which are of relevance to this study as follows:

- is the service providing what people really need?

- what effect does the service have on the lives of users and their carers?

- is it possible to tell whether the service has made any difference to what users are able to do and the way they feel?

- are there any easy, straightforward ways in which funding bodies, service providers, users and carers can regularly check on the impact of the service?

Nocon *et al.* conclude by saying:

> '*Just providing services is not enough. We need to know whether they do in fact meet people's needs. We need a way of routinely monitoring the impact of what is provided so that any mismatch between what people need and what is on offer can be put right ... [users and their carers] must have a say in assessing the effectiveness of the services. After all, users are best placed to say what difference services have made to their lives.*'

The last few decades have seen a substantial increase in both the range and extent of community and social services, as well as a growing realisation of the importance of evaluating the quality of these services. *Shaping a Healthier Future: A Strategy for Effective Health Care in the 1990s* (Department of Health, 1994) set the challenge of measuring the quality of services as one of its targets. This challenge was to be met by constantly monitoring and evaluating quality through various means, including clinical audit and customer surveys, and by monitoring service outcomes to ensure that they were as effective and efficient as possible.

While acknowledging that Irish health services, including those specifically provided for older people, were of a high standard and were managed by committed and caring staff, *Shaping a Healthier Future* did state that:

> '*Many of the services are not sufficiently focused towards specific goals or targets and it is therefore difficult to assess their effectiveness. The information which would support this focusing is frequently unavailable or, if available, is under-utilised.*'

The 1994 Health Strategy placed an explicit onus on health providers to monitor, evaluate and re-orientate if necessary, services for older people, to ensure that optimum service is provided for those who might require it.

The Eastern Health Board (now the ERHA) was also conscious that evaluation and measurement of quality have become more important. In its *Ten Year Action Plan for Services for Older Persons 1999-2008* (Eastern Health Board, 1998), the Working Group recommended that all new service developments for older people should be evaluated as soon as possible after they have been put into place. As part of its mandate to put in place 'systems, procedures and practices to enable it to monitor and evaluate services' (*Health* (Eastern Region Health Authority) *Act*, 1999) the ERHA is currently drawing up standards for residential services for older people.

Following on from this theme, Brenner and Shelley (1998), points out:

> 'All programmes require evaluation, initially of feasibility and later of process and outcome. Older people themselves should be encouraged to become involved in research projects. Programmes which are positively evaluated need to be sustained and used as models elsewhere.'

Two major interrelated factors contributing to the increasing realisation of the importance of evaluation have been the growing voice of the consumer and the growing demand for quality community services. However, the HeSSOP report found that, in Ireland, efforts to consult with consumers in the health and social system have been limited. It describes how, when there is a consumerist approach to consultation, people are only given limited opportunities for involvement and participation. They are being asked to evaluate output without an explicit explanation of the reasons for and results of that evaluation.

The National Council on Ageing and Older People (Garavan *et al.*, 2001; Delaney *et al.*, 2001; Ruddle *et al.*, 1997) has argued that democratic models of consultation be adopted and that evaluation programmes focus on, among other things, quality of life outcomes for the client.

This model proposes that service users should take an active role in the decision-making process, including the way in which services are developed, structured and provided. In evaluation programmes that have at their centre quality of life outcomes, evaluations must focus on how well the needs of the client are met, and service users must be consulted during the development and planning of those aspects of the evaluation.

Regular evaluation of services at all levels is essential if services are to become more effective and more appropriate to individual older people. In *The Years Ahead Report: A Review of the Implementation of its Recommendations* (Ruddle *et al.*, 1997) the authors stressed the importance of evaluating the effectiveness of day services in order to determine standards and principles of good practice.

In the past, and even today, the evaluation process has often been regarded by service planners and providers as an enormous burden. Evaluation was often seen as a unique and complex process occurring at a certain time in a certain way, and almost always involving outside experts. It was often perceived to be about proving the complete success or total failure of a programme.

Programme evaluation methods were often chosen largely on the basis of achieving complete scientific accuracy, reliability and validity. As McNamara (1999) and many others have described, this approach often generated extensive data from which very carefully chosen conclusions were drawn. Generalisations and recommendations were avoided. As a result, evaluation reports tended to reiterate the obvious and left service planners and providers disappointed by the process.

Evaluation can be confused with other related activities such as assessment, monitoring, reassessment or quality assurance. This difficulty is referred to in some detail in *Care and Case Management for Older People in Ireland* (Delaney *et al.*, 2001). As the authors point out, all these activities involve examining aspects of a service or a programme and are linked to the evaluation process (e.g. quality assurance relates to actions *following* service evaluation), but are not substitutes for evaluation *per se*.

52

1.11 Day Services for Older People: A Preliminary Classification

The Consultative Committee of the NCAOP felt that, in order to inform this report, it was important to attempt a preliminary classification of day services for older people in Ireland, given the historical interchange of terms and its resulting confusion (Table 1.1). As the focus of the report is the broad policy aim of day service as an ongoing social support for older people, rather than short-term rehabilitation support or protective supervision, it was decided that the parameters of study would exclude day services such as day hospitals and psychiatric day hospitals, where duration of attendance is intended to be short-term, and include those categories where attendance is expected to be ongoing and indefinite.

This Preliminary Classification of Day Services in Ireland, which examines primary and secondary objectives, staffing, management, selection of older people, duration of attendance and funding, is intended as a preliminary categorisation. It is a first step in the generation of a system to classify services that most clearly reflect the real nature of day services in Ireland. It is not in any sense meant to be a definitive classification, but rather an initial attempt to enable categorisation of facilities participating in this study that can then be revised in the light of the findings.

While acknowledging that many facilities may cross two or even three models, day services were classified by the Consultative Committee as four preliminary categories: day care centres; day centres; social clubs; and dementia-specific day centres. However, the Consultative Committee acknowledged that some models may have different descriptors, for example, social clubs may also be known as senior citizens' clubs or active retirement groups.

Table 1.1: Preliminary classification of day services in Ireland

Facility	Primary objectives	Secondary objectives	Staff	Health board management or direction	Selection of older people	Duration of attendance	Funding
Day care centre (day-care service)	To support independent living among disabled or socially isolated older people Assistance with personal care and health care	Maintenance of function Carer respite Social interaction	Health-care professionals +/- multi-disciplinary team or part thereof	Under direction of Services for Older People section	Referral from PHN, GP or community care and hospital inpatients on discharge from the hospital Care of the Elderly team	Indefinite	Health board funded
Day centre (social satellite centre)	To facilitate social interaction Personal development	Personal care (minor) Carer respite +/- episodic health initiatives	Volunteers/ local council/ voluntary group or religious community	Under own direction	Open selection: membership defined by themselves	Indefinite	Partial health board funding

Table 1.1: Preliminary classification of day services in Ireland (continued)

Facility	Primary objectives	Secondary objectives	Staff	Health board management or direction	Selection of older people	Duration of attendance	Funding
Social club (senior citizens' club or active retirement group)	To facilitate social interaction	Further education Personal development	Volunteers and members	Under own direction	Open selection: membership	Indefinite	No health board funding
Dementia-specific day centre/day-care (Alzheimer's centre)	Protective and appropriate supervision for older people with dementia Carer respite	Personal development Social interaction/ activities Personal care	Volunteers (paid or unpaid) +/- nursing/ physiotherapy	Under direction of Alzheimer Society/ Western Alzheimer Foundation or similar	Open selection: membership decided by centre	Indefinite	Partial health board funding

The Preliminary Classification of Day Services in Ireland attempts broad descriptions of the objectives of the four models of day service: these range from supporting independent living among disabled or socially isolated older people to facilitating social interaction and to providing protective supervision for older people with dementia. However, the components required to achieve the service objectives of day facilities must be more clearly defined so that older people and their carers know what to expect from each type of facility, and that those referring older people will direct them to the facility most appropriate to their needs and preferences.

The Years Ahead (Department of Health, 1988) report recommended that the Department of Health prepare guidelines for the operation and management of day centres. To date, such guidelines have not been introduced. Undoubtedly, one of the reasons for this is the lack of clarity in so many areas. If day services for older people are to become core services, then they must be subject to regulation, in order to ensure that quality of service is consistent in all areas. Service contracts setting out the obligations of both the health board and the voluntary organisation providing the service must be drawn up. Finally, as Ruddle *et al.* (1997) points out, funding procedures must be formalised and standardised across the country and must be based on accepted criteria.

In order to refine service objectives and the components of service delivery required to achieve them, it is necessary to know what older people and their carers want and expect from the various day care services and facilities. It is increasingly recognised that the service should fit the needs of the older person, rather than the other way round. Putting people at the centre when it comes to delivery of care, and supporting and encouraging them to be involved in their own health care, is a central tenet of the Health Strategy *Quality and Fairness* (2001). Success in this area means listening to older people themselves and not simply assessing their needs from the views of those referring to and delivering services.

Ruddle *et al.* (1997), in their consideration of both the value and deficits in day care services for older people, concluded that the perspective of the older users of day services is a vital research area which needs to be addressed. It is the aim of this study to do this by consulting older people and their carers, and also by taking into account the views of service providers who work in day facilities and Public Health Nurses, as well as older people in the community who do not use such day facilities.

Older people, like others sectors of the population, are not a homogeneous group. Their needs, capabilities and interests vary greatly. Determining what types of people use or want to use day services will inform the design of services to accommodate differing requirements and the development of service objectives targeted to these requirements.

On foot of the need to develop targeted service objectives and the components of service delivery needed to fulfil those objectives, there is the need to consider the question of evaluation. Ruddle *et al.* (1997) strongly recommended the importance of evaluating the effectiveness of day services in order to determine standards and principles of good practice.

The aims of the study are:

1. to develop service objectives and the components of service delivery required to achieve those objectives, for each type of facility under investigation.
   To meet this aim, five sets of consultations were carried out with the following groups:

   - older people who use day care centres, day centres, social clubs and dementia-specific day centres

   - older people in the same communities who do not use these day facilities

   - family carers of older people

   - service providers working in these facilities including managers, care attendants, drivers, volunteers and visiting therapists and professionals including physiotherapists, chiropodists and hairdressers

   - Public Health Nurses

2. to propose appropriate evaluation processes which will allow the facilities to be evaluated at strategic intervals

3. to formulate recommendations relevant to health and social care policy with regard to the future development of day care services in Ireland.

Chapter Two

The Research Process

59

Chapter Two
The Research Process

2.1 Introduction

The main aims of the study are to develop service objectives for different types of day facility, to detail the components of service delivery needed to fulfil those objectives and from this to suggest appropriate evaluation processes which will allow the facilities, in all their dimensions, to be evaluated at strategic intervals.

In order to meet the aims of the study, consultations were carried out in fifteen different day facilities with:

- older people who use day care centres, day centres, social clubs and dementia-specific day centres

- older people living in the same communities who do not use these facilities

- family carers of older people

- service providers in day facilities

- Public Health Nurses (PHNs).

2.2 Selection of Day Facilities

Fifteen day facilities from all over Ireland were selected to take part in the study. In order to take account of variations in populations, and urban/rural, statutory/voluntary and facility type dimensions, seven facilities were selected from the Eastern Regional Health Authority (ERHA) area (two from the East Coast Area

Health Board; three from the South Western Area Health Board; two from the Northern Area Health Board), two from the Southern Health Board area and one each from the remaining six health board areas. Some of the centres are health board facilities and others are managed by voluntary organisations. These facilities were identified as being representative of the spectrum of day facilities available throughout the country.

Having identified these facilities, the centre managers were approached and the aims and logistics of the study explained to them. They all agreed to participate in the study.

2.3 Classification of Day Facilities

Of the fifteen centres selected for the study, it was possible to classify nine at the outset using the criteria of the Preliminary Classification of Day Services in Ireland model (Table 1.1). Four of these centres were clearly day care centres in terms of their aims, statutory sector management, selection and funding. Using the same criteria, one was clearly a social club and two were clearly dementia-specific day centres. A further two were predominantly day centres, although in both there were some older people who were only attending for the purpose of social interaction rather than for any of the other characteristics of day centres, such as minor personal care or carer respite.

The remaining six centres, which were originally identified as either day care centres or social clubs (in terms of their members, and therefore, *a priori*, in terms of their services and their aims), clearly included many of the characteristics of two, and sometimes even three, categories detailed in the Preliminary Classification of Day Services in Ireland. It is also the case that within these six centres the differences between them were sometimes as marked as the similarities. This point is discussed further in Chapter Five.

In order to attempt the process of developing service objectives and the delivery components required to achieve those objectives, as well as to impose some level of structure on a sector lacking clear definitions, it was decided (for the purposes of this study) to discuss these six facilities together. This does not imply that they all have the same criteria, are uniquely different from other types of facilities or even that they are rigidly labelled. It simply means that (for the purposes of this study) they do not neatly fit into any of the other, more formally defined, categories in the Preliminary Classification. Indeed, they are probably typical of many day services for older people throughout the country that have evolved from their original purpose and are now providing a somewhat different mix of services. It could be said that they are, in fact, achieving an outcome supported in the Health Strategy *Quality and Fairness* (2001), by putting the person at the centre in the delivery of care and fitting the service to the needs of the older person, rather than the other way round.

Using the features of the Preliminary Classification of Day Services in Ireland model discussed in Chapter One, the fifteen centres visited are described as:

● four statutory sector day care centres (see Chapter Three)

● two voluntary sector day centres (see Chapter Four)

● six voluntary sector day care centres/social clubs (see Chapter Five)

● two voluntary sector dementia-specific day centres (see Chapter Six)

● one voluntary sector social club (see Chapter Seven).

It is very important to point out that even within these categories, all fifteen centres had developed due to a combination of factors which influenced their present stages of development and would continue to be reflected in their ongoing and changing development. These factors, along with others such as the range of health services, social services and transportation services available to older people in the locality are not constant. The complexity of these interactions means that classifying these facilities can only be done with a degree of caution (Table 2.1).

Table 2.1: Classification of facilities

Location	Statutory/Voluntary	Facility type
ERHA – ECAHB	Statutory	Day care centre
EHRA – ECAHB	Voluntary	Day care centre/social club**
EHRA – SWAHB	Voluntary	Dementia-specific day centre
EHRA – SWAHB	Voluntary	Day care centre/social club **
EHRA – SWAHB	Statutory	Day care centre
EHRA – NAHB	Voluntary	Day centre
EHRA – NAHB	Statutory	Day care centre
SHB	Voluntary	Day care centre/social club*
SHB	Voluntary	Day care centre/social club**
WHB	Voluntary	Dementia-specific day centre
MHB	Statutory	Day care centre
SEHB	Voluntary	Day care centre/social club***
NWHB	Voluntary	Day care centre/social club**
MWHB	Voluntary	Day centre
NEHB	Voluntary	Social club

* This centre has both a full day care centre and a separate social club. Therefore, for the purposes of this study, it has been described as a day care centre/social club.

** These centres have full or close to full day care facilities. However, they also have a more mixed portfolio of services and activities than those centres classified as day care centres. Therefore, for the purposes of this study, they have been described as day care centre/social clubs.

*** This centre sees itself as a social club. However, it also provides some day care services to more vulnerable older people. Therefore, for the purposes of this study it has been described as a day care centre/social club.

2.4 Fieldwork

From the middle of June to the middle of August 2002, visits were made to the fifteen facilities and consultations were carried out with:

- 78 older people attending day facilities

- 23 older people in the community not attending the facility but where the manager or local PHN felt that attendance would benefit the older person or family carer

- 20 family carers

- 47 service providers at different levels in day facilities

- 14 PHNs.

Table 2.2 shows the numbers of older people and family carers consulted in each of the fifteen facilities.

Table 2.2: Numbers of older people and carers consulted

Facility	Older people attending	Older people not attending	Family carers
ERHA – ECAHB	5		1
ERHA – ECAHB	6	3	1
EHRA – SWAHB	5		
EHRA – SWAHB	6		1
EHRA – SWAHB	6	2	1
EHRA – NAHB	6	2	1
EHRA – NAHB	5	2	1
SHB	3	3	3
SHB	5	2	1
WHB	3		2
MHB	5	1	2
SEHB	6	2	1
NWHB	7	2	1
MWHB	5	2	3
NEHB	5	2	1
Total	78	23	20

Table 2.3 shows the numbers of service providers and PHNs consulted in each of the fifteen facilities. Service providers have been classified as manager/member of voluntary committee, care attendant/care worker and other service providers including drivers, cooks and hairdressers.

Table 2.3: Numbers of service providers and PHNs consulted

Facility	Manager/ member of voluntary committee	Care attendant/ care worker	Others	PHNs
ERHA – ECAHB	1	1	1 (physiotherapist)	
ERHA – ECAHB	2	1	1 (hairdresser – volunteer)	
EHRA – SWAHB	1	3		2
EHRA – SWAHB	1		1 (cook)	
EHRA – SWAHB	1	1	1 (chiropodist)	
EHRA – NAHB	1	1	1 (driver)	1
EHRA – NAHB	1	1	1 (driver)	1
SHB	2	1	1 (driver)	2
SHB	1	2		1
WHB	2	2		1
MHB	2	1		1
SEHB	1		1 (cook – volunteer)	1
NWHB	2		1 (cook)	1
MWHB	1	1		1
NEHB	1		3 (project co-ordinators)	2
Total	20	15	12	14

Of the 47 service providers consulted, 15 were centre managers, 5 were senior members of the local voluntary management committee, 15 were care attendants (care workers, professional carers) and 12 were other service providers (including drivers, cooks, hairdressers and visiting professionals).

The procedures for obtaining consent, the consultation process and the consultation themes varied for each group.

2.5.1 Consultations with Older People Attending a Facility

The older people who participated in the study were selected by a variety of means. In the two dementia-specific centres, the managers identified older people in the early stages of dementia where consultation would be possible and meaningful. In the remaining thirteen centres, older people were identified by a combination of discussion with the manager and observation in the centre. When the older person was approached, the researcher introduced herself and briefly outlined the purpose of the study. In total, 79 people were approached and 78 gave their consent to participate in the study.

The main themes during consultations with older people attending the centres were:

- information relating to their attendance at the facility, including number of days a week and number of hours a day in attendance, transport arrangements, services of which they availed and participation in activities

- their views on services and activities – what they liked and didn't like, and how services and activities could be improved

- issues of loneliness and companionship

- demographic data including age and marital status.

At the end of each day, the recorded notes were transferred to a consultation record in order to facilitate analysis of both the qualitative and quantitative data generated during the consultation.

2.5.2 Consultations with Older People Not Attending a Facility

Consultations were carried out with 23 older people not attending a day facility. Their consent to take part in the study was requested by either the centre manager or the PHN.

The main themes during consultations with older people not attending the centres were:

- reasons for not using the centre

- views as to why other older people use the centre

- issues of loneliness and companionship

- demographic data including age and marital status.

As before, the recorded notes were transferred at the end of each day to a consultation record.

2.5.3 Consultations with Family Carers

Consultations were carried out with family carers whose loved ones attended a centre, who were preparing an older person for a first visit to a centre, or who were in the process of trying to persuade an older relative to attend a centre. In the majority of cases (fourteen) the carer was the sole carer. Just over half the family carers (eleven) also cared for their own family. None of the carers worked full-time outside the home and three worked part-time.

The main themes during consultations with family carers with an older person attending a centre were:

- how often the older person used the centre, whether the carer would like to see the older person use the centre more often, as well as the carer's opinion regarding the current transport arrangements

- satisfaction with the services and activities provided

- the importance of the centre to the life of the carer.

The main themes during consultations with family carers with an older person not attending a centre were:

- reasons for not using the centre

- whether the carer would like to see the older person attending day care and whether it would support the carer.

As before, the recorded notes were transferred to a consultation record.

2.5.4 Consultations with Service Providers

The main themes during consultations with service providers were:

- various aspects of service provision including days and times of opening, staff numbers and categories, management and funding, transportation arrangements and service charges

- categories of older people attending the centre

- provision and quality of services and activities

- older people's input regarding programmes and management

- perceptions of the value and deficits of day care.

As before, the recorded notes were transferred to a consultation record.

2.5.5 Consultations with Public Health Nurses (PHNs)

Managers were asked to inform their local PHN about the study and invite them to take part. The main themes during consultations with the PHNs were:

- perceptions of the value and deficits of day care

- the services that should and could be provided in each type of day centre setting, as well as views on core services

- issues such as opening hours and transport

- views on the unfulfilled demands for day care.

The main findings of the consultation process are presented from Chapters Three to Seven. Additional findings are presented in Appendix A.

Chapter Three

Consultations in Day Care Centres

Chapter Three

Consultations in Day Care Centres

3.1 Introduction

In order to meet the aims of the study, consultations were carried out in four statutory day care centres. Table 3.1 shows the numbers of people that were consulted.

Table 3.1: Consultations in day care centres

Category	Numbers
Older people attending centres	21
Older people not attending centres	5
Family carers	5
Service providers	12
PHNs	2

3.2 Consultations with Older People Attending Day Care Centres

The older people attending day care centres were consulted in some detail about the time they spent in there, and the aspects and services that they valued and enjoyed most. There were ten aspects or services that were of most significance to them. They were, in order of importance:

- enjoyment of peer company

- staff

- meals

- activities

- transport

- hair-care

- baths/showers

- chiropody

- physiotherapy

- respite for carers.

3.2.1 Enjoyment of Peer Company

Without a doubt, the most important service provided by day care centres according to the older people consulted, is the opportunity to meet, talk with and undertake activities with their peers. Many of them described their days in the centre as the highlight of the week when they got up early, made a special effort to dress smartly and to be ready when their transport arrived. Typical comments included:

> *'If I didn't have this place I would be lost ... [it] keeps my mind going, keeps me from thinking too much ... [I] love the company, the craic.'*

> *'The company is the most important thing – great to get out for a day and chat to other people.'*

3.2.2 Staff

The staff, whether managers, care attendants, drivers, volunteers or occasional providers such as hairdressers and chiropodists, are enormously important to the older people. As several service providers pointed out, for many of these older people especially those living alone, they are possibly the only dependable and capable adults they come into contact with during the week.

The older people know that they can trust the staff to turn up with the bus, provide a meal and help them with hair-care, nail care and shopping. More than that, they can be trusted with problems, difficulties, family misunderstandings and many aspects of the older people's personal lives that they cannot discuss with anyone else:

> *'The manager is marvellous. She will enquire about our problems and make phone calls for us if we are having difficulties getting services.'*

> *'Lovely people who work here, all so cheerful, and cheer us up.'*

3.2.3 Midday Meals

For older people, sharing a meal is a very important aspect of day care activity. In all the centres (except the social club) there was a lot of emphasis on eating and drinking. The quality and quantity of the food is important, but so is the social aspect. For many, it is the only time when they eat either with others or with their peers. With very few exceptions, the older people were pleased with their meals:

> *'The food is beautiful, best of food, plenty and piping hot.'*

> *'I come for a meal every day and I love it.'*

> *'The meal is great – great to have a day when I don't have to cook my own.'*

3.2.4 Activities

There is no doubt that what the majority of older people attending day care centres enjoy most is social conversation, whether this is on the bus, over a cup of tea or a meal, sitting in groups or as part of an organised activity such as playing bingo or cards.

Musical activities of all sorts are also very important to older people in day care centres. These include singing, dancing, listening to a visiting musician or doing gentle exercises to music. Other popular activities include playing cards and bingo:

> *'Love the cards with my six pals. Like the sing-songs. Only play bingo when there is no one to play cards with.'*

3.2.5 Transport

Providing appropriate transport, with a suitable driver, is an extremely important service in both urban and rural areas. Without this transport, services would often be inaccessible. Almost all of the older people attending the day care centres relied on the transport services provided by them:

> 'Love coming on the bus … up to an hour each way, but always singing and great fun.'

> '[I] would like it if the bus could come every day but it can't so I pay for a taxi three days a week.'

> 'The driver is a wonderful man. He talks about football. He is a fishing man – used to fish myself.'

3.2.6 Hair-care and Baths/Showers

Hair-care, including hair washing, cutting, setting and drying, is a very important service for many of the older people, particularly (but not exclusively) the women. Across all the facilities in the study, about one third of the older people consulted use this service, rising to more than half the people attending day care centres:

> 'I get my hair done and that is brilliant. [I] get it done every week.'

Overall about one fifth of the older people consulted regularly had a shower or a bath in the centre, with this figure rising to about one quarter of the older people consulted in day care centres. For these people, even though they are in a minority, it is a very important service. Many of them, even those with carers, pointed out that they found it either very difficult or physically impossible to have a bath or a shower at home:

> '[I] love to have a shower here and feel great.'

> 'I can manage a shower at home but it is a great service for those who cannot do it themselves – a most essential thing especially for older men living alone.'

3.2.7 Chiropody and Physiotherapy

About one third of all the people consulted used the chiropody and physiotherapy services, and most thought them to be useful and important services. However, one of the logistical difficulties encountered is that older people can regularly miss out on these services if they are provided on a certain weekday when there is no transport available. As one older person explained:

'I would use the chiropodist but she comes on a different day to my day – however, my neighbour cuts my toenails so I'm okay.'

Only two out of the four day care centres offer physiotherapy. Where the service is available it was generally well regarded. However, the lack of physiotherapy in day care centres (and in other facilities as well) was more keenly felt and created difficulties for some older people. This was the one area in which older people were most critical:

'Physiotherapy was good but the service has now stopped.'

'There is no physiotherapy. This is a great disadvantage as many of us could really do with regular physiotherapy. Centre is supposed to be getting [a physiotherapist] but no sign so far.'

3.2.8 Respite for Carers

Just under half the older people consulted for this study and attending day care centres are living with members of their family, whom many, but not all, regarded as their 'carers'. For a few of these older people, particularly those whose high physical dependency is combined with good mental health, there is an awareness that their coming to the centre provides much needed time for the carer as well as a change of environment for themselves:

'[It] gives my wife a break – she can get out and doesn't have to worry about me.'

3.3 Consultations with Older People Not Attending Day Care Centres

3.3.1 Reasons For Not Using a Day Care Centre

The older people were asked their reasons for not using a day care centre. Several older people gave more than one reason.

All of the older people consulted regarded themselves as content at home and not needing to go to the local day care centre. Several saw themselves as self-sufficient, independent and able to occupy themselves through, for example, reading, walking and gardening. A typical explanation was:

> 'I don't need anything. I am a good reader. I have good health – physical and mental. I am religious and accepting, comfortable in my own little home.'

A second reason for not attending which was given by two people was that they would feel insecure away from home due to an illness or a debilitating condition. One older woman had osteoporosis and other health problems, and felt that she would be a nuisance and a burden. Another felt that the centre was too far away and she would not be able to get home when she wanted to.

The one older man consulted was very negative about the range of activities available at the day care centre. He repeatedly described them as:

> 'very monotonous and boring. They are very dull and not active.'

The older people were asked if the centre might interest them at some time in the future, for example, if their health were to deteriorate. The majority had not given this question any thought and a few thought that they might consider it, but there did not appear to be any great enthusiasm for this prospect.

3.3.2 Reasons Why Other Older People Use Day Care Centres

The older people not attending day care centres were asked for their views as to why other older people would use these facilities. They felt primarily that attending a day facility might help lonely or depressed older people to cope with loneliness and isolation. Some of them acknowledged that centres are 'good places' with good facilities for those that want or need them. There was recognition that they are places for company, chat and a meal, and fine for people who 'like that kind of thing' and who 'don't mind the long day'.

3.3.3 Feelings of Loneliness and Isolation

The older people not attending day care centres were asked about their own feelings of loneliness and isolation. None of them admitted outright to such feelings, however several did refer to their attempts to prevent them. Others just find the burden of being old and sick difficult:

'I miss chatting to other people but I try hard to be happy.'

'[I] never get lonely – don't I have the television?'

'[I] don't get lonely, just very sore and in pain. This osteoporosis is a big nuisance.'

3.4 Consultations with Family Carers

Consultations were carried out with five family carers. Four of the five older people being cared for had dementia, and one was a man in good mental health whose mobility has been seriously impaired by a stroke. The aspects of day care that were most important to family carers were:

- respect for their relatives

- personal care

- transport

- social activities

- differences to the life of the carer.

3.4.1 Respect for their Relatives

Over and above everything else, family carers are primarily concerned that their loved ones will be treated with gentleness and respect in a safe and secure environment. This is important for all carers, but particularly those caring for older people who have dementia:

> 'It is very important for me to know that she is safe and well looked after. If the day ever comes and I have to put her into permanent care, then I will be happy about the home next door because the same people work in both places and I trust them.'

> 'They treat him with great respect – this is very important for him because he was such a lively, busy man before his stroke and now he is very immobile, but they don't treat him like an invalid.'

3.4.2 Personal Care

Family carers, especially those with older people in day care centres (as well as day centres and dementia-specific day centres), thought without doubt that personal care was the most important service provided. For many carers, the whole process of bathing, showering and hair-care is a major difficulty because of either mobility restrictions or behavioural problems associated with dementia. A typical comment was:

> 'My wife has a shower and they do her hair. Some days she nearly drives me mad if I try to do it myself.'

3.4.3 Transport

Of the five family carers consulted, four were able to avail of transport provided by the centres. For three of these carers, all older women, this was very important as they themselves would have had great difficulty getting their relative to the centres. One younger woman drives her mother to the centre herself, although transport is available. Her mother, who has dementia, cannot be rushed and it is easier for her daughter to take her.

3.4.4 Social Activities

The family carers, especially those caring for older people with dementia, did not have a great deal to say about the social activities available other than they hoped their older relatives found them interesting and stimulating. For most of these carers, the fact that the older people could attend for a few hours, have a meal, a shower and their hair done in a safe and caring environment, was enough for them without being too prescriptive about activities. The carer of one older person who did not have dementia was very content with the social activities:

> 'He enjoys all the activities, especially learning to play bridge.'

3.4.5 Differences to the Life of the Carer

It was a feature of many of the family carers consulted at all types of facilities, that the needs and concerns of the older person being cared for were expressed before their own. Comments such as these were not infrequent:

> 'They are all wonderful to her – she joins in the craft circle and they make her feel just like one of the others. These two days a week are very important to me and I am happy with that for now.'

> 'I find it wonderful because not only can I get out and do things on the two days he is there, but also he enjoys himself and is well looked after.'

For many carers the few hours per day, or even per week, were the only time when they could relax from the responsibilities, demands and fatigue of constant caring. For some family carers, both here and at other centres, talking to the researcher was a very emotional experience and several wept while discussing the loneliness, isolation and difficulties of their own lives.

With very few exceptions, the carers consulted were not demanding or critical of either the service they received from their centre or the services they received in general. This may reflect the fact that family carers traditionally receive and expect very little help. It is important to note that a recent Comhairle social policy report on carers, which included interviews with representatives of the Carers' Association and health board carer co-ordinators, reported that availability and opening hours of day care centres were regarded as inadequate and did not facilitate carers wishing to return to work (Comhairle, 2002).

The main themes expressed during consultations with service providers can be summarised as follows:

- funding, management and staffing

- categories of older people attending

- services provided

- social activities provided

- respite for carers

- care plans for older people.

3.5.1 Funding, Management and Staffing

The four day care centres are funded and managed by the respective health boards. Staffing was a major problem in three of the four centres. Several of the service providers complained of having insufficient time to provide the quality of service that they would like to provide and to which they feel the older people are entitled. As one manager expressed it:

'We are understaffed and there are days when we crawl out of here on our hands and knees.'

In a second day care centre, the manager felt the staff would not be able to cope without the thirteen volunteers, mostly elderly women from the community, who come in to help serve the thirty midday meals:

'We are very vulnerable if any of us gets sick. When I go on annual leave, the cook is then in charge.'

Managers and care attendants felt that they had insufficient time for talking, listening, and social interaction with the older people:

'The time element for chatting is very important and often we are so busy that we don't have enough time for this and we are conscious of that. We do the best we can but we need more staff.'

All the day care centres (and, indeed, all of the facilities participating in this study) have a daily service charge paid directly by the older people. The charges (which include, for example, the meal) are not standard and vary from €4 to €11 per day. Sometimes the service charge includes transport but at other times this is extra. Small additional charges are sometimes requested, perhaps for morning or afternoon tea or a bingo book.

3.5.2 Categories of Older People Attending

The older people attending these four centres formed quite a mixed group, with most having some degree of physical or mental dependency. They included people who were depressed, people who were physically active but lonely or isolated, people who were wheelchair-bound, people who were post-stroke and people in the early stages of dementia.

In each of the centres there was a small number of individuals who, when first referred for a specific health gain, would have needed quite a high level of support through activation and maintenance. They have now reached the stage where they no longer need this level of support and could leave, releasing a place to someone on the waiting list. However, their enjoyment of the social aspects of the centre, such as companionship, makes them reluctant to move on. As one manager put it:

'What we need here are two different centres – one high support and one with more social activities for those who don't need the support any more but want the companionship.'

All four centres had a few older people in the early stages of dementia, and at least one centre had one or two people at a more advanced stage. One centre was prepared to accept people with early dementia providing they did not have severe incontinence. Another accepted a few people with early dementia but received very few referrals. The reason for this was unclear. A third centre had a good relationship with the local Alzheimer's Society, which runs a special programme in the centre on Saturday mornings for older people with dementia. Both service providers and carers at this centre report that this support is very important in helping them to care for older people with dementia.

Two centres had a few 'younger' older people with severe mobility difficulties caused, typically, by an illness such as multiple sclerosis. It was felt by the service providers that day care centres were not appropriate places for these people. Although many of their needs and those of their family carers were being met through the personal care and nursing services, their social needs, in terms of appropriate stimulation, were often neglected.

3.5.3 Services Provided

The services provided by the day care centres can be divided into three categories: those provided in all four centres; those provided in some centres; and the numerous individual services that are provided at a personal level.

Table 3.2: Services provided in day care centres

Services provided in all centres	Services provided in some centres	Individual services at a personal level (examples only)
Transport	Nursing (3 centres)	Accompany to hospital appointments
Midday meals	Chiropody (3 centres)	Collection of pensions and prescriptions
Hair-care	Physiotherapy (2 centres)	Money management
Baths/showers	Occupational therapy (2 centres)	Banking
	Laundry (1 centre)	Visits when in hospital and assistance in visiting each other in hospital
		Telephone calls to statutory and voluntary agencies
		Assistance with some or all shopping
		Accompany to funerals

3.5.3.1 Transport

Each of the four centres has its own transport facility, at least in theory. All four centres are located in built-up areas (one in central Dublin, two in suburban Dublin and one in a large rural town). The service providers felt that traffic is one of the main difficulties encountered in collecting and returning older people. As one manager described it:

> 'We have only one bus and one driver, so although our driver is working from 9 to 6, by the time he gets the country people in and then gets back for the town people, the day is half over.'

Another issue raised was the capacity of the buses. At one centre, the bus is so small that it has to be supplemented by two taxi runs. Very often the taxi that is sent out is not wheelchair-compatible, and there have been several occasions when older people and their carers have been left disappointed. This finding was supported by one of the drivers in a second centre who found that, because the bus is so small, he is 'making several runs a day and this makes their day short'.

3.5.3.2 Midday Meals

The four day care centres provide three-course midday meals, as well as morning and afternoon tea. In one centre there is a choice of main course. Morning and afternoon teas, accompanied by bread, scones or biscuits, are also served in all the centres.

All the service providers consulted in the day care centres strongly believed that providing a nutritious, well-cooked and well-presented meal was hugely beneficial to the older people, both physically and socially. They know that many do not cook for themselves and that they are eating at least one good meal on the days they come to the centre.

In two of the day care centres meals are prepared on the premises, and in the others they are delivered from nearby residential units. The service providers felt that this arrangement did not affect the quality of the meals provided, but it did mean that with the delivered meals there was less control over portion sizes and individual preferences. This can at times be upsetting, especially if an older person has a difficulty with a particular food or food type.

Hair-care was regarded as an important service by providers in the four day care centres. For many older people, especially those with disabilities and those living alone, hair-care, like foot-care, can be very problematic.

In all four centres a hairdresser visits to wash, cut and set hair. The facilities for this service vary from the reasonably well-equipped to the very poor where, in one centre, the hairdresser is required to attend to the older people in a bathroom. Although the service providers in this centre regarded the bathrooms as spacious, they felt that hair-care offered in this environment is not a quality service.

Although all four centres have the facilities to offer baths and showers, in one the service is offered with a certain lack of enthusiasm. This may be partly to do with pressures on staffing:

> 'We are not the bathhouse of [name of area]; we do not do baths or showers as a routine, because it is not necessary. We only do it if there is an accident or if the client finds it absolutely impossible to do [this] at home.'

83

In the other three day care centres, under similar staffing pressures, the service was seen as somewhat more central or the approach to it was more understanding and flexible. In one, it was recognised that although most of the older people would have bath/shower facilities at home, these might be upstairs and difficult to access. In another the service was described as 'vital', especially for some of the older men. In this particular centre the shower is in a small dark room that has no toilet and no room for a hoist.

3.5.3.4 Nursing

Although it is usually health board policy, or at least practice, for day care centres to be nurse-led this was not the case in one of the four statutory day care centres consulted for this study. However, there is a good working relationship between the local PHNs and the manager of this centre.

In the three nurse-led day care centres nursing services are seen as more central than in the other types of facility, whether nurse-led or not. Even though the older people attending the day care centres would, in terms of their age and physical and mental health, be comparable to those attending the two day centres (see Chapter Four), the service providers tended to place more emphasis here on practical tasks such as dispensing medicines, giving injections, providing nebulisers, seeing to dressings, and recording blood pressure and blood sugar levels. This is not meant to imply that these services are unavailable in the other centres, but rather that they were discussed with lesser importance, if at all.

3.5.3.5 Chiropody, Physiotherapy and Occupational Therapy

Chiropody is offered in three of the four day care centres. The fourth, according to the manager, does not offer chiropody because all the older people have, and prefer to see, their own chiropodists. This centre is located in an area where chiropody facilities are very good.

The service providers in the other three centres regarded chiropody as a vital service. Access to the service and its availability varies and, in the views of the service providers, ranges from very satisfactory to very poor. As one manager described it:

> 'Chiropody is a very poor service at present: we only get a couple of hours once a month and we might have maybe fifteen or so [older people] all lined up. They don't pay much, but they don't get much either.'

Several service providers including a chiropodist, observed that men, as well as being generally more reluctant to come to day care centres, are also more reluctant to have their feet attended to.

One of the difficulties encountered in day care centres (and also in other facilities) is where a professional, such as a chiropodist, always visits on the same day of the week. This often means that those older people attending on a different day miss these visits. In one centre this difficulty has been overcome by arranging with the chiropodist to vary his monthly visit so that he covers all five days. Everyone now has an opportunity to see the chiropodist at least once every five months.

All the service providers in the day care centres regarded physiotherapy as a vital service, but it was available in only two centres and regarded as a quality service in only one. In two of the centres, despite repeated efforts, there was still no physiotherapy service available:

'Physiotherapy is a problem … none, and no sign of [the] health board giving us one; many of them need it and have to go elsewhere. It would be great if they could get it here.'

'We have no physiotherapist … used to have one but not any more … just cannot get one … same with occupational therapy.'

Service providers in three of the four centres regarded occupational therapy as an important service but not as vital as physiotherapy. It was only provided in two centres but in both was regarded as a good service.

3.5.3.6 Laundry

Only one of the four day care centres provided a laundry service, which was described by the service providers as 'vital', particularly for older men living alone. It was said that there was no demand for such a service at the other three centres.

3.5.3.7 Individual Services at a Personal Level

Apart from the services already discussed, every day care centre provides a range of individual services that can vary enormously between different centres and individuals. To the service providers, these individual services allow older people to retain control over their own lives and affairs, and help them to maintain a sense of dignity and independence.

3.5.4 Social Activities Provided[3]

In all the day care centres consulted, the main social activities were quite similar. These included bingo, card games, gentle exercise programmes to music and other musical activities including sing-songs, dancing or entertainment provided by volunteer musicians or each other.

Apart from these main social activities, each centre had other popular activities, for example, crosswords, basket-weaving or playing bridge. Often these more unusual activities reflect the interests of a current or past member, service provider or volunteer and have thrived through their enthusiasm and endeavours.

Several of the service providers spoke about the challenges of motivation, as they perceived it. They observed that more than anything, the older people enjoy sitting

---

3   Across all fifteen centres, from the highly active social club to the dementia-specific day centres, there is a broad range of social activities (see Appendix B).

and chatting. Sometimes it can be difficult to motivate them because they just want to talk or read the newspaper. The service providers find that one older person with motivation can 'get things going' for an entire group.

One of the managers held very much a minority view on social activities. She argued that social activities should be nurse-led, as it is necessary to be aware of the patient's condition in order to make an input. In her view, care attendants must be happy with a combination of patient care and domestic work.

All of the other managers saw the role of care attendants as central, if not crucial, to a successful programme of social activities. As one manager expressed it:

> 'Our care attendant does crafts with them: she is brilliant at that. We get them framed and you can see them all around the walls.'

The input from volunteers was discussed. Several of the service providers observed that they would benefit from outside help with the social activities programme but it is much more difficult to get volunteers than in the past:

> 'We might meet someone who has a skill that we think would be of interest and we ask them to donate some of their time but everyone is too busy.'

One centre is making tentative plans for a seven-day service in the future. The staff feel that it is wasteful of resources for the centre to be totally empty at weekends and would like to encourage a programme of social activities on these days.

3.5.5 Respite for Carers

Most of the service providers consulted in day care centres see day care as not only offering respite to carers but also providing them with a network of support, allowing them to discuss their difficulties and to hear about other services from the centres. Some would like to advance this support. One manager reported:

> 'We are thinking of setting up a service here for carers who work. Many carers of [the] highly dependent who work find day care not very useful. This service would go from 8am to 6pm and would be a real support for those who need to work and want to keep their older people in their own home.'

3.5.6 Care Plans for Older People

When asked about care plans for older people, several of the service providers seemed to regard this as synonymous with ongoing monitoring of health status indicators, such as monthly weighing and recording of blood pressure and blood sugar levels. This was particularly the case in the three nurse-led centres, where a considerable degree of paperwork is done. It was less apparent in the fourth non-nurse-led centre.

3.6 Consultations with PHNs

The two PHNs who were consulted felt that day care centres, and other types of day facilities, were successfully supporting older people in the community and their carers with regard to most aspects of care.

Waiting lists were of concern in both centres where the PHNs worked. In the first, a different catchment area is catered for each day and so people based in rural areas can only attend once a week, which according to the PHN was unsatisfactory. The PHN in the second centre observed:

> 'The centre is very good but the waiting list is long. We have a high proportion of over-75s in this area. Their needs are great. The only turnover really comes from mortality and not from people moving into long-term care. Indeed, half of the regulars should be coming in more than one day a week, but we cannot offer it to them.'

Many of the service providers consulted for this study complained about staff shortages. This point was reiterated by the PHNs who felt that both centres needed not only more staff but also more staff with the right qualifications.

Persuading older men to attend day care centres (and other forms of day centre) can be a challenge. Both PHNs pointed out that this does not apply so much to high dependency men who, through a combination of their own needs and those of their carers, may have no alternative to day care other than long-term institutional care. The issue is more apparent with men with low dependency levels, particularly if they are living on their own.

3.7 The Primary and Secondary Objectives of Day Care Centres

Consultations for this study confirmed that day care centres play a critical role through the services they provide directly to older people, the network of support given to older people and their carers, and through contact with other health and social agencies, in helping to keep older people in their own homes for as long as is possible or practicable.

The four core services provided in all four centres were seen, with very few exceptions, to be vitally important in supporting older people. Combined with individual services at a personal level, the nursing and therapeutic services offered in or accessed through the centres and the social activity and stimulation programmes, these services were fundamentally important to the older people and their carers.

From these in-depth and wide-ranging consultations, it is clear that the primary and secondary objectives of day care centres, as shown in the Preliminary Classification of Day Services in Ireland (Table 1.1), can be refined.

The *primary objectives* of day care centres are:

● to prevent older people from going into long-term care

● to support independent living among older people

● to provide assistance with personal care and health care

● to facilitate activation/social interaction

● to provide support and respite for carers

● health promotion.

The *secondary objectives* of day care centres are:

● to maintain function

● to provide health, social care and welfare services information

- to facilitate personal development

- to provide individual services at a personal level.

These objectives, and the structural and process components of service delivery required to achieve these objectives, will be further discussed in Chapter Eight.

3.8 Gaps and Deficits/Challenges

There is no doubt that day care centres can offer numerous health and social benefits, but a number of gaps and deficits have been identified and discussed. Many of these gaps are directly related to the low level of secure funding.

These include:

- insufficient numbers of day care centres resulting in long waiting lists

- understaffing

- inadequate transport facilities

- lack of availability of certain services, such as physiotherapy

- limited support for carers

- unsuitability for certain categories of older people, such as those with more advanced dementia

- unsuitability for 'younger' older people with physical disabilities

- inappropriateness for those older people no longer in need of a high level of support but relying on the social supports

- motivation difficulties

- lack of appeal for many men.

The Department of Health and Children, as well as many health boards have acknowledged that the provision of day care centres is inadequate (*Quality and Fairness*, 2001).

Understaffing is a problem besetting many sectors of service. The Bacon report (2001) on current and future trends in the supply and demand of physiotherapists and occupational therapists, concluded that a major expansion in the numbers of therapy professionals is essential over the next 15 years.[4]

Transportation difficulties for older people requiring care services have been frequently recognised (Moffatt, 2000). The need for more support for carers is a regular call from many organisations, such as the Carers' Association and Comhairle (2002) and statutory reports (*Listening to the Voice of Carers*, South Eastern Health Board, 2000).

A recurring issue was the inappropriateness of day care centres for several categories of older people. They include those with 'difficult' dementia (i.e., those who may wander, suffer with incontinence or display agitation), those 'younger' older people with physical disabilities and older people who no longer need a high level of support through activation and maintenance but have come to rely on the social supports.

Several service providers spoke of difficulties in motivating older people towards social or recreational activities. However, when the older people themselves were consulted for this study, no conflict was found. Activities allowing them to interact socially with one other were the most popular. These findings are supported by an ongoing Midland Health Board review of day care services which has found that the most popular recreational activities are entertainment, followed by bingo, outings (where available) and playing cards.

The reluctance of older men to come to day care centres (and to other types of day service, as the following chapters will discuss) is a phenomenon that has been observed in this study by service providers, PHNs and older people themselves.

---

4   In May 2002, on foot of the Bacon report, Mr Micheál Martin, Minister for Health and Children, announced the provision of 175 extra professional therapy training places for students to tackle the acute shortage of physiotherapists, occupational therapists, and speech and language therapists in the health service.

Chapter Four

Consultations in Day Centres

Chapter Four

Consultations in Day Centres

4.1 Introduction

In order to meet the aims of the study, consultations were carried out in two voluntary day centres. Table 4.1 shows the numbers of people that were consulted.

Table 4.1: Consultations in day centres

Category	Numbers
Older people attending centres	11
Older people not attending centres	4
Family carers	4
Service providers	5
PHNs	2

4.2 Consultations with Older People Attending Day Centres

The outcome of the consultations with the older people attending day centres was very similar to that obtained from consultations in the four day care centres in Chapter Three. The aspects and services important to older people, such as enjoyment of peer company, the services provided, the staff, meals and social activities, are equally important to those attending both types of facility.

4.3 Consultations with Older People Not Attending Day Centres

As in Chapter Three, these older people were asked their reasons for not attending a day centre. Several of them gave more than one reason, but they all felt content at home and not in need of day care.

Feeling insecure away from home due to an illness or condition, was an issue raised a number of times by older people who don't, or won't, attend day care centres or day centres. In one case, a 'younger' older man in his late sixties who had had a stroke thirty years earlier (affecting his speech and mobility), had always been looked after very well by his wife, who was his sole carer. She was now very unwell and needed a break from caring for him. He was frightened that if he went to the centre nobody would understand what he was saying or what he wanted. He felt that he would be at the mercy of other people's authority and he would lose what little control he had over his own life.

These older people again felt that going to a day centre might help lonely or depressed older people to cope with loneliness and isolation. They acknowledged that centres had 'good facilities for those that want them' and that 'they are fine for older people who want to attend'.

4.4 Consultations with Family Carers

As with the family carers consulted at the day care centres, the aspects of day care that were most important to family carers were:

- respect for their relatives

- personal care

- transport

- social activities

- differences to the life of the carer.

One of the family carers referred to the fact that for her, just knowing that the service was there and available, helped her face up to future difficulties that she would inevitably experience:

'Even though my mother only comes in one day a week, the knowledge that she could come in five days if I need it. [It] is so reassuring just to know that this is here. It is just invaluable. At the beginning there was no light at the end of the tunnel, but now it is possible to keep her at home because I know that I have this service if and when I need it.'

4.5 Consultations with Service Providers

The main themes expressed during consultations with service providers can be summarised as follows:

- funding, management and staffing

- categories of older people attending

- services provided

- social activities provided

- respite for carers

- care plans for older people.

4.5.1 Funding, Management and Staffing

In the two voluntary day centres, the bulk of funding comes from the health boards, primarily in the form of wages for the manager, the bus drivers, the care attendants and the cook. Other sources of funding include service charges, donations and fundraising. One of these centres has FÁS support for a secretary, a cleaner and an activities worker:

'By and large it works quite well, except that FÁS keeps taking its people off for training. This is fair but can leave us very short-staffed.'

4.5.2 Categories of Older People Attending

The older people attending these day centres were very similar in profile to the older people attending the statutory day care centres. They included people in the following categories:

- post-stroke

- physically active but lonely or isolated

- wheelchair-bound

- early dementia.

4.5.3 Services Provided

The services provided by the day centres can be divided into three categories; those provided in both centres; those provided in one centre; and those individual services that are provided at a personal level.

Table 4.2: Services provided in day centres

Services provided in both centres	Services provided in one centre	Individual services at a personal level (examples only)
Transport	Nursing	Accompany to hospital appointments
Midday meals	Aromatherapy	Collection of pensions and prescriptions
Hair-care		Money management
Baths/showers		Banking
Chiropody		Visits when in hospital and assistance in visiting each other in hospital
		Telephone calls to statutory and voluntary agencies
		Assistance with some or all shopping
		Accompany to funerals

4.5.3.1 Transport

In both day centres, the managers were reasonably satisfied with their transport facilities. Each centre owns a bus with wheelchair capacity, ramp and lift. Any transport problems tend to result from traffic. This is particularly acute in the more urban of the two centres, where some of the older people are sitting in the bus for up to an hour or more each way. This, in the manager's view, was very unsatisfactory. Traffic difficulties mean that some older people attending this centre cannot be picked up and, in some cases, the family pays for a taxi.

4.5.3.2 Midday Meals

The two day centres, like the day care centres, provide three-course midday meals, as well as morning and afternoon tea. One of the centres prepares its meals on the premises and the other has them delivered from a nearby hospital. This does reduce costs for this particular voluntary organisation, but because of the small staff numbers in relation to the numbers of older people, serving the meals is a very slow process. The older people do not complain, but the staff find this situation quite unacceptable. This organisation has looked for voluntary help from the community but to little or no avail. Last year it produced a circular encouraging members of the community to help with a range of activities in the centre, including serving meals, but the response was very poor.

4.5.3.3 Hair-care and Baths/Showers

Both centres offer a hair-care service. One has a very pleasant and nicely appointed hair-care room. The other centre is older and has no space for a dedicated room, so here the older people are taken to a hairdresser in the locality. The service providers seem happy with this situation. However, none of the six older people consulted in this centre had used the hairdresser, or seemed to know very much, if anything, about the service.

Although the quality of the facilities varies greatly between these centres – one has a Parker bath and the other has a rather cramped space without a window or an extractor fan – the bathing and showering service is regarded as very important. As one care attendant pointed out:

> 'Even something as simple as coming here once a week for a bath can mean the difference between coping at home and having to go into care.'

4.5.3.4 Chiropody

As with the service providers in the statutory day care centres, the day centre managers regarded chiropody as an essential service. Both centres offer this service and both sets of service providers were happy with it. In one centre the chiropodist attends once every three months but, because the visit is well organised, the manager felt that the service is satisfactory.

4.5.3.5 Nursing

The requirements of the older people attending the day centres were very similar to those of the older people attending the day care centres. In both of these centres, even though one is nurse-led, there seemed to be less emphasis on medical needs *per se* and slightly more emphasis placed on spiritual, social, psychological and, in one centre in particular, practical needs.

4.5.3.6 Aromatherapy

In one centre, hand, neck and foot massage using aromatic oils, is highly regarded as a form of relaxation, especially following gentle exercises. This is a time-consuming activity for the care attendants and, again, the centre has tried unsuccessfully to find volunteers with an interest in aromatherapy to come in and help.

4.5.3.7 Services Not Offered

Laundry and physiotherapy, which are offered in some of the day care centres, are not offered in these two day centres. Both managers reported little demand for a laundry service, but one regarded the lack of physiotherapy as a drawback:

> We did have a physiotherapist but we cannot replace her, so the service is now very poor. We have funding for an occupational therapist but we have no room to provide the service.

The other manager felt that as both physiotherapy and occupational therapy are available in the nearby hospital it is not necessary for the centre to duplicate these services.

4.5.3.8 Individual Services at a Personal Level

As in the day care centres, the day centres offer a large number of individual practical services at a personal level according to need, demand and available time (see Table 4.2 for the typical services provided).

4.5.4 Social Activities Provided

The main social activities in these two day centres are similar to those in the four day care centres. They are essentially passive in nature and include gentle exercise programmes to music, sing-songs, entertainment from volunteer musicians, bingo and quizzes.

The topic of motivation recurred during consultations. All the service providers spoken to reiterated that the older people enjoy, more than anything, sitting and chatting. Some providers were more concerned about this than others. In one centre it was referred to positively as 'informal chat-based reminiscence', but the manager of the second centre was a little more anxious:

> 'They often seem to find the meal and the chat the most important aspects of the day. It can sometimes be very difficult to get them to do things. We find that sometimes if a key person in a particular group – such as crafts – dies, then the activity dies with them and it can take a long, long time to remotivate them again.'

In both of these centres (as in many of the other facilities visited), service providers reported that spiritual sessions such as prayers, Mass, Communion and other devotional activities were very important to the older people.

4.5.5 Respite for Carers

All the service providers agreed that day services for older people are very important for family carers. The carers repeatedly tell them how much they appreciate the days they have for themselves and how important these breaks are. However, as one manager pointed out, life with a family carer may also be difficult for the older person.

The service providers have, on rare occasions, come across cases of physical and mental abuse of older people by a family carer. In these instances, taking an older person into a day centre can mean removing them from real or potential harm.

A more frequent occurrence reported by service providers is loneliness:

> 'Older people can be dreadfully lonely, even when living with other family members. I know cases where this service made all the difference between staying at home or going into long-term care.'

4.5.6 Care Plans for Older People

When asked about care plans for individual older people, one manager replied:

> 'No, we don't believe in this. This is a social activity centre not a medical unit.'

The second centre does have care plans, especially for the more dependent people attending. It does a lot of work with post-stroke older people, both in the centre and in their homes. One of their care attendants is a member of the District Care Team and her role is to assist post-stroke people to help themselves with walking, dressing, feeding themselves, and getting in and out of bed. If she has a problem she can call on any member of the District Care Team for assistance.

4.6 Consultations with PHNs

As with the PHNs consulted in the four day care centres, both PHNs consulted in the two day centres were appreciative of the roles played by day facilities in supporting both older people in the community and their carers.

One of the PHNs raised recurring concerns regarding long waiting lists, understaffing and the reluctance, not only of men but also sometimes of women to come to day services. This particular centre was located in an inner city area, which would be considered as having a range of social, economic and community problems:

> 'Stigma is a problem – stigma of area and stigma of being seen to be old and dependent. Older people have this view that only poor and doddery old people use day care.'

At the same time, this centre has a long waiting list and can frequently only offer an older person one day a week which, in the views of both the PHN and the service providers, is totally inadequate.

The centre is located in an area where the facilities for older people with dementia are very poor, and the centre staff often find themselves under pressure to accommodate such people. The PHN explained:

> 'If they are difficult or disruptive nobody wants them. There are very few places where they can go. But they cannot upset the rest of the clientele in a day care centre. If the centre has an open door policy, like this one, they cannot be taken if they need to be watched.'

This situation occurs in many day facilities. Service providers come under pressure to accept older people with dementia in their centres but, because they do not have the necessary staff or facilities to meet such special needs, they often have to refuse. PHNs understand this but are also under pressure to find suitable services that can cater for the special needs of these older people.

4.7 The Primary and Secondary Objectives of Day Centres

There are considerable similarities between the four statutory day care centres discussed in Chapter Three and the two voluntary day centres discussed in this chapter and, not unexpectedly, the results of both sets of consultations were very similar.

The consultations with older people in day centres and in the community, family carers, service providers and PHNs, again confirmed that day centres play a critical role in supporting older people in their own homes for as long as is possible and practicable.

The services provided in the two voluntary day centres were very similar to those provided in the statutory day care centres. From these consultations it is clear that the primary and secondary objectives of day care centres, and the gaps, deficits and challenges as presented in Chapter Three, are also applicable to day centres.

Chapter Five

Consultations in Day Care Centres/Social Clubs

Chapter Five

Consultations in Day Care Centres/Social Clubs

5.1 Introduction

Six of the fifteen facilities participating in this study clearly straddled two, and sometimes three, categories as defined in the Preliminary Classification of Day Services in Ireland. In order to attempt the process of developing service objectives it was decided, for the purposes of this study, to discuss these six day care centres/social clubs together. Table 5.1 shows the numbers of people that were consulted.

Although all six centres are unique and probably have as many differences between them as similarities, one is quite different from the others. Unlike the other five, which responded to local needs as dictated by local structural circumstances (such as lack or availability of transport and facilities), this centre has a determined policy of social inclusion and integration. Through its defined day care and social activities programmes, it has set out to cater for low, medium and high dependency older people and those needing no care at all. It has established services, programmes and activities that are geared towards older people but not used exclusively by them. The service providers see themselves as running services in the locality to be used by people in that locality.

Table 5.1: Consultations in day care centres/social clubs

Category	Numbers
Older people attending centres	33
Older people not attending centres	12
Family carers	8
Service providers	18
PHNs	5

5.2 Consultations with Older People Attending Day Care Centres/Social Clubs

The older people were consulted in some detail about the time they spent in their centre, as well as the aspects and services they valued and enjoyed most. There were five major aspects or services that were of most significance to them. They were, in order of importance:

- enjoyment of peer company

- activities

- meals

- personal care (hair-care, baths/showers, chiropody)

- transport.

5.2.1 Enjoyment of Peer Company

The most important service that day care centres/social clubs provide, from the perspective of older people, is undoubtedly the opportunity to meet, talk with and do a range of things with their peers, the service providers, the volunteers and other members of the community they meet both inside and outside the centres:

> '[I] would be round the twist if I didn't have this place. The whole
> atmosphere is great from top to bottom. It is like a little oasis. If you have
> a problem you can talk about it but nobody makes false promises. I like
> that. Nothing is a problem to the manager – she has a great way.'

5.2.2 Activities

The range of social activities provided in these centres is much wider than is
typical in the day care centres and the day centres. Many of these activities
involve a great deal of effort, concentration, motivation and application. However,
it is important to remember that many of the older people attending these more
diverse centres/clubs are very similar to the more dependent people attending
day care centres and day centres. For this reason, more passive activities such
as bingo and sing-songs, are also offered and enjoyed in most of them.

For some of the more active older people attending day care centres/social clubs,
especially the more geographically isolated women, the opportunity to pursue their
own personal activities in the local village or town is what they enjoy most:

> 'As soon as the dinner is over, I'm off to the bank, the shops, the post
> office, [or to] have a chat with somebody.'

> 'The bus is great – after the meal it takes us shopping, to the hairdresser,
> the doctor, dentist or bank. Our driver will carry the shopping for us into
> the bus with no complaints at all.'

5.2.3 Midday Meals

Throughout the consultations with older people there was little criticism of any
aspect of the meals service. The very few adverse comments came mainly from
those attending the day care centres/social clubs:

> '[The] meal is okay but could do with variety just to make it more
> interesting … something to spice it up … Monday always the same,
> Tuesday always the same. On the other hand it's great value.'

> 'Meals are alright as value for money, but it would be nice to have a bit
> of a change. We get soup everyday.'

5.2.4 Personal Care (Hair-care, Baths/Showers, Chiropody)

Many of the older people attending the day care centres/social clubs were interested in some aspects of the personal care service. Whether they were frail or active, coming in for a full day or just a short period, they were very positive about having their hair and their feet attended to.

There were a number of active older people, especially 'younger', older widowers or single men, who drove in several days a week for a meal and company, and who had no interest in any of the personal care services. One older man, a retired businessman, said:

> 'I have plenty of money. I could eat in a restaurant every day if I wanted to. But to come here and eat with my friends, that is the best part of my day. At the weekends I eat in restaurants and it is very lonely.'

5.2.5 Transport

Many of the older people reported that transport was their 'lifeline' to the rest of the world. Even though some of the journeys, particularly in rural areas, can be very long (up to a hour each way, which is far too long, according to the service providers), none of the older people consulted reported any difficulty with this. On the contrary, they often reported the bus journey as a time for conversation and socialising.

5.3 Consultations with Older People Not Attending Day Care Centres/Social Clubs

Consultations were carried out with twelve older people in the community who were not attending the centres. Among them were three older people who seemed to have very little need of any of the services provided, and two who were carers would have had great difficulty getting out to the centre. Apart from these people, most of the other older people consulted reported similar reasons for not using the centres to those discussed in previous chapters.

Consultations were carried out with eight family carers. All were women caring for mothers, fathers or husbands. Three of these carers were hoping their family members would be allocated a place at a centre in the near future, so as yet they had no experience of the facility. Four of the remaining five were caring for older people with mild to moderate dementia.

The aspects of the services most important to these family carers were very similar to those already discussed:

- respect for their relatives

- personal care

- transport

- social activities.

106

As was the case with other carers, these women tended to voice the needs and concerns of their relative before their own:

> 'Although I could probably cope with my mother at home all the time at this stage, I very much appreciate the centre, partly because it allows me to get on with work at home, but mostly because it is just so good for my mother. She loves coming and I am very happy about that.'

The three carers who were hoping their family members would soon attend the centres were all attending a carers' course, which the centre runs from time to time. They all found that coming to the centre and talking to other people made it easier to cope with their difficulties and the anxieties that their older family members had about attending.

The main themes expressed during consultations with service providers can be summarised as follows:

- funding, management and staffing

- categories of older people attending

- services provided

- social activities provided

- care plans for older people.

5.5.1 Funding, Management and Staffing

The six day care centres/social clubs are variously funded by health boards, fundraising, service charges, FÁS, Community Employment schemes, corporate donations, EU schemes etc., with the proportions varying considerably from one centre to another.

One centre, for example, is run by a parish-based organisation, with staff funded by the health board, operating in premises owned by the city council and supported by one part-time FÁS worker, one full-time Jobs Initiative worker and thirty volunteers.

In another centre, which is managed by a voluntary organisation with charitable status, only the manager's salary and a small grant are received from the health board. Most of the other staff are paid for by FÁS:

'Our main anxiety at the present moment is the cutting of FÁS staff – we are enormously dependent on them. This is very difficult for a voluntary committee to deal with – we don't want to get into the position of being employers with all that that entails. We don't know what we are going to do and it is very upsetting because we don't know what is happening. Will the health board take them on and do we want that anyway?'

In a third centre, the original capital came from the managing voluntary organisation, but all current funding now comes from the health board, with the exception of small service charges for meals and transport. This centre does not have a written agreement but agreed a budget with the health board which, in the opinion of the manager, was working well.

5.5.2 Categories of Older People Attending

The older people attending these centres were from a very wide range of categories – from those with mild/moderate dementia needing care and whose carers needed respite, to active older people who attended under their own steam (walking or driving their own cars) and lively, but geographically and socially isolated, older people needing company and a lift into town for shopping, banking and meeting up with friends.

Many women, particularly those living in rural areas, suffer geographical and social isolation, especially when the acute lack of public transport in rural areas is combined with the fact that many older Irish women do not drive. For these people, going to the centre one day a week offers them a trip into town in the minibus.

Unlike the centres described in previous chapters, where the older people tended to come for the 'full' day, the patterns of attendance in the day care centres/social clubs varied greatly. Some of the more dependent older people would attend for a full day's care or carer respite. The more active might walk in or drive themselves in for the meal, the activities, a musical afternoon or to meet friends. They might come in one evening a week for a personal development course, line dancing class or to sing in the choir.

An example of this 'mix' can be found in one of the centres which provides, on average, 180 main meals per week (36 per day), but when it looks at everyone coming to the centre for all activities and services, including after-hours activities, it is catering for an average of 270 people each week.

5.5.3 Services Provided

The services provided by these centres can be divided into three categories: those provided in all centres; those provided in some centres; and other individual services.

Table 5.2: Services provided in day care centres/social clubs

Services provided in all day care centres/ social clubs	Services provided in some centres	Individual services (examples only)
Midday meals	Hair-care (5 centres)	Opportunities for older people to access facilities such as shopping and banking
Chiropody	Showers/Baths (5 centres)	Opportunities for older people to get involved in fundraising
	Transport (5 centres)	Opportunities for older people to exercise their talents such as writing poetry, quality craft-making
	Laundry (5 centres)	
	Physiotherapy (3 centres)	
	Nursing (3 centres)	
	Occupational therapy (2 centres)	

5.5.3.1 Midday Meals

For many of the more active older people with greater control over when they came and went, it was the midday meal that appealed most to them. Coming in for the meal was often encouraged by the service providers as a way of keeping in touch with these older people who, although often quite active and independent, might have an aspect of their personal lives which made them a little vulnerable. For example, some of the service providers reported that widowed men, who were still relatively young and healthy, might have difficulties shopping for and cooking a proper meal. For these older people, coming to the centre for meal a few times a week, or even every day, was a positive nutritional and social experience. Older people who lived close enough to walk to the day care centre/social club also fell into this category.

One of the day care centres/social clubs is fundamentally different from the others. Unlike the other facilities, where there is little or no choice regarding the menu, this centre has a canteen which is used by everybody: the older people themselves (high, medium and low dependency); staff; visitors; family carers; and those attending for events, lectures or courses. This is a deliberate policy not only to promote social inclusion but also empowerment, even if it is only empowering older people to choose their own food. This, as the chief executive of the centre explained, is fundamental to the philosophy of this centre, which is to help and encourage older people to make their own decisions.

5.5.3.2 Chiropody, Physiotherapy and Occupational Therapy

A chiropody service is offered, at least in theory, in all six centres. In four of the centres, however, the service providers were not happy with the service. In one centre, where the chiropody facilities are normally very good, the manager commented:

> 'At the present moment chiropody is very unsatisfactory - our usual very good person is out on maternity leave and the replacement has just rung to cancel again for the third week in a row. Huge demand for this service is building up. We need someone at least once a fortnight, at least.'

In another centre, where again the facilities are good, the managers complained about how difficult it was to get the chiropodist to attend more than once every three months. From their point of view, this is not satisfactory.

Physiotherapy is offered in three of the centres with a fourth hoping to offer it very soon. This service will be offered in conjunction with the local health board. It will be a service for the community but will be based in the centre. This statutory/voluntary partnership for providing a physiotherapy service already works well in another centre. The two centre managers unable to offer a physiotherapy service regarded this as a deficit. Both have been trying to involve the health board in a partnership, but so far without success.

Only two of the six centres offer occupational therapy. In the remaining centres this absence is not seen as a major deficit. As one manager put it:

> 'We have no occupational therapy but, if the physiotherapist thought it was necessary, she would include it.'

5.5.3.3 Hair-care, Baths/Showers and Laundry

Five of the six centres offer a hair-care service. In the sixth, hair-care is no longer provided and there is no demand for it. This centre is located in a large town and draws many of its members from the immediate environs, where hair-care facilities are plentiful.

In the five centres where hair-care is provided, the facilities vary from state-of-the-art (with a fully-equipped, professionally-designed, purpose-built room) to poor and ill equipped. However, regardless of the equipment and facilities available, the older people availing of the hair-care service clearly enjoyed it. One hairdresser explained:

> 'Hairdressing is a very important service; I have the best equipment, anything that I want. However, I have been coming for 12 years, two to three times a week, and what these older people want more than anything else is time to chat. A little chat is very important.'

Five of the centres have bathing/showering facilities and the sixth would like to offer this service. Less than one fifth of the older people consulted in the day care centres/social clubs actually used the bath/shower service. Nevertheless, most of the service providers regarded it as an important service. This is the case even in those day care centres/social clubs that see themselves as being more concerned with 'social activity'. The facilities for offering baths/showers vary enormously:

> 'Our bathroom is excellent. We designed it ourselves. It is huge, with a Parker bath, and has everything that one could possibly need.'

> 'We even have to use our tiny shower room for storage and then take it all out every time we want to give someone a shower. It's a real nuisance.'

Five of the six centres offer a laundry service although one manager described the centre's service as 'very small and not in much demand'.

5.5.3.4 Transport

Five of the six centres have their own transport, which ranges from 'good' to 'just satisfactory'. The manager of the only centre without its own transport viewed this as a distinct disadvantage:

'We have no bus of our own. We rent a minibus twice a week but it has no wheelchair access [and it] does not collect at houses, so people have to make their way down to the road. Volunteers will collect in nearby areas if necessary. [I] sometimes feel that some families could be a bit more helpful in getting older people into the centre. And it is getting more and more difficult to get reliable volunteers to drive.'

5.5.3.5 Nursing

In five of the six day care centres/social clubs, even those that are nurse-led, much more emphasis is placed on the social model of care than on overt nursing care and monitoring. The single exception to this is the centre described at the beginning of this chapter, which has adopted a somewhat different approach to care.

In this group of centres, the emphasis is on social activities and the recreational aspects of personal care, such as getting hair cut or set, as opposed to simply keeping it kept clean. As one of the managers explained:

'Just because a person is a senior citizen does not mean that they lose the ability to live vibrant, self-sufficient lives and most of them do. Only when an individual can no longer cope in one area does care, in that area, come into operation.'

This is an observation of fundamental importance because it recognises that if an older person requires assistance with a particular facet of their life, such as having a bath or cooking a meal, it does not render them dependent in every other aspect of their life.

5.5.4 Social Activities Provided

The range of social activities provided is much wider in the day care centres/social clubs than is typical in the day care centres and the day centres. As well as the more sedentary activities found in the other facilities, the activities in these day care centres/social clubs often involve a higher level of physical activity. Examples include indoor bowling, line dancing, creative dancing, darts and keep fit classes. Some activities are introduced with a particular aim, such as putting on a choral or dramatic production, learning a new skill such as making a video or producing a newsletter or a book of poems.

In several centres these activities have a dual purpose: they provide the older people with stimulation and enjoyment, while often raising money for the centre. In one centre, the older people run a second hand clothes shop; in another, the annual output of the sewing circle is raffled at the Christmas sale; in a third, they grow plants which are later sold at an auction. The proceeds are often used to fund or subsidise outings, Christmas and birthday parties.

In one of the centres there is a strong emphasis on learning and development. It offers courses in personal development, relaxation techniques, diet and exercise, health and safety, and computers and Internet access. This centre, which has run exchange programmes with centres in France, Germany, South Africa and Italy, recently introduced the Silver Threads Scheme, which it has borrowed from its Italian contacts. This scheme encourages keeping in telephone phone contact with older people who cannot, or will not, come to the centre.

5.5.5 Care Plans for Older People

When asked about care plans for older people, one manager summed up the general feeling of a number of centre managers:

> *'Individual care plans are often there but are carried around in people's heads. To me that is fine. Just because they are beautifully written up does not make them any more valid – on the contrary sometimes. If the PHN is involved she does an assessment of needs anyway; that is a basic part of any individual care plan. The fact of the matter is that having discussions with clients and carers takes time and resources.'*

5.6 Consultation with PHNs

All five PHNs consulted were generally supportive of the roles played by these centres in particular, and by other types of day centres in the lives of older people and their carers. The PHNs reiterated observations made by their colleagues regarding gaps and deficits including insufficient numbers of centres, long waiting lists, understaffing and difficulties in providing quality physiotherapy services in some places.

Several PHNs made the point (borne out by this study) that very often the facilities that exist are good – there are just not enough of them. One PHN said:

> 'This centre is a beautiful little centre, perfectly located in the middle of the town: beside the church, the bank, the shops and the post office. However, it is far too small. We only have the one centre and so people can only come one day per fortnight. This is not really enough [but] better than nothing but we would love it if everyone could come at least one day a week.'

The reluctance of older men to attend the centres was raised again by several of the PHNs.

5.7 The Primary and Secondary Objectives of Day Care Centres/Social Clubs

Perhaps the outstanding strength of the six centres discussed in this chapter, is the variety, flexibility and range of services and activities they offer. The categories of older people attending are wide-ranging; the patterns of attendance are often varied and flexible; the services provided differ from one centre to another; and the range of social activities includes opportunities for greater input from the older people themselves.

The *primary objectives* of day care centres/social clubs are:

- to prevent older people from going into long-term care

- to facilitate social interaction/social activities

- to encourage personal development

- health promotion.

The *secondary objectives* of day care centres/social clubs are:

- to provide minor personal care

- to provide health, social care and welfare services information

- to support and respite for carers

- to provide individual services at a personal level.

These objectives, and the structural and process components of service delivery required to achieve these objectives, will be discussed in Chapter Eight.

5.8 Gaps and Deficits/Challenges

The gaps, deficits and challenges identified and discussed in these six centres include:

- insufficient numbers of centres

- long waiting lists

- understaffing

- anxiety over the possible loss of Community Employment schemes, Jobs Initiative programmes and FÁS-funded jobs

- difficulties in providing quality services, particularly physiotherapy

- the reluctance of older men to attend the centres.

Almost all of the centres consulted during the study had problems with understaffing, but several of the managers also anticipated increasing difficulties with the loss of Community Employment schemes, Jobs Initiative programmes and FÁS funded jobs. Current funding levels are not adequate to employ staff to replace those working on these schemes, if and when they leave. This is a challenge affecting not only voluntary day services for older people but the wider community and the voluntary sector.

Traditionally, this sector has depended on volunteers to provide a huge range of services. Since the early 1990s, as Ruddle and Mulvihill (1999) documented in considerable detail, far fewer people have been able to volunteer their time and services. This study has confirmed the anecdotal evidence from many voluntary organisations that finding, and holding onto, good volunteers is becoming increasingly difficult. There is little evidence to suggest that this decline will be reversed in the foreseeable future.

Community Employment schemes and Jobs Initiative programmes have, over the last few years, helped to fill the breach caused by the declining numbers of volunteers.

Without secure funding for the provision of adequate numbers of trained staff at all levels, including care attendants, drivers, cooks and cleaners, many voluntary sector centres which are currently providing the backbone of services, may be forced to cut back rather than expanding and developing their day services for older people.

Chapter Six

Consultations in Dementia-Specific Day Centres

Chapter Six

Consultations in Dementia-Specific Day Centres

6.1 Introduction

In order to meet the aims of the study, consultations were carried out in two dementia-specific day centres. Table 6.1 shows the numbers of people that were consulted.

Table 6.1: Consultations in dementia-specific day centres

Category	Numbers
Older people attending centres	8
Older people not attending centres	N/A
Family carers	2
Service providers	8
PHNs	3

6.2 Consultations with Older People Attending Dementia-Specific Day Centres

Consultations were carried out with eight older people attending the dementia-specific day centres. Five were described by the service providers as having early stage dementia and three whose dementia was at a more advanced stage. All eight responded to questions about their ages, their living and travelling arrangements, and marital status. Those in the early stages responded to some questions about their activities, the services provided, and what they liked and disliked. They discussed whether or not they enjoyed, for example, their meals, getting their hair done, singing old-time songs and saying prayers. For those in the more advanced stages most, if not all of these questions, were more difficult to respond to.

Observing the older people, in their interactions with each other and with the service providers during the day's activities and programmes, tended to be more informative than attempting detailed consultations. The fact that most of the older people seemed to be occupied and content (although there were some exceptions in both centres) was attributable to the attention and vigilance of the service providers.

In all of the centres visited for this study, the service providers were notable for their flexibility and imagination: managers who cooked; cooks who did the cleaning; cleaners who helped with social activities; drivers, chiropodists and hairdressers who acted as counsellors, confidantes and friends. Nowhere was this more apparent than in the two dementia-specific day centres. Having this flexible, team effort approach to services and activities, and allowing the older people to do what they want whenever possible, seems to produce centres with an atmosphere of calm and little sign of agitation.

Nevertheless, it must be remembered that unlike the majority of older people attending other types of day facilities, older people attending dementia-specific day centres have very little choice regarding whether or not they attend, how many days they attend and how long they stay. Allowing them to decide whether or not they want to dance, paint or have a bath, is perhaps as much empowerment or control over their own lives as they ever get.

6.3 Consultations with Family Carers

Consultations were carried out with two family carers. In common with all the other family carers (many of whom were also carers of older people with dementia), the most important aspect of day care is that their relative is treated with respect and dignity in a safe, secure environment. Also of great importance to carers was the personal care available. As one young woman expressed it:

'They shower her, do her hair and change her clothes; she won't let me do that. I try to shower her but she won't give in. She won't change her clothes for me. I would be burnt out if [I/she] did not have this place, would not have coped, would have had to made other arrangements.'

6.4 Consultations with Service Providers

The main themes expressed during consultations with service providers can be summarised as follows:

- funding, management and staffing

- categories of older people attending

- services provided

- social activities provided

- respite for carers

- care plans for older people.

6.4.1 Funding, Management and Staffing

Both dementia-specific day centres are run under the auspices of voluntary organisations and receive funding from a number of sources. One centre has been able to attract more funding than the other, with the result that it has a more secure staff and better facilities. In the other centre, there was anxiety concerning the possible termination of the Community Employment Scheme. This centre, which was understaffed and had no replacement for the manager when she was not present, had four Community Employment Scheme workers.

6.4.2 Categories of Older People Attending

As would be expected, almost all of the older people attending the two dementia-specific day centres had varying degrees of dementia, but occasionally an older person with mental health difficulties would attend.

One of the centre managers felt strongly that although her centre looked after older people with varying degrees of dementia, it was not a suitable place for those in the early stages. She felt that the activities could be dull, and that these older people would find a day care centre or social club more stimulating.

6.4.3 Services Provided

The services provided by these centres can again be divided into three categories: those provided in both centres; those provided in one centre; and other individual services at a personal level.

Table 6.2: Services provided in dementia-specific day centres

Services provided in both centres	Services provided in one centre	Individual services at a personal level
Midday meals	Transport	Accompany on walks or drives
Hair-care	Chiropody	Accompany to the shops
Baths/showers	Physiotherapy	
Nursing		

6.4.3.1 Midday Meals

Both centres provide midday meals. Unlike the other types of facility, the dementia-specific day centres see very little 'coming and going' during the day. Usually when older people attend, with rare exceptions, they attend for the entire day and, therefore, the meal is an essential service.

In both centres (although the food preparation, cooking and serving facilities are at opposite ends of the spectrum in terms of space and equipment) there is an emphasis on the importance of flexibility and personal preference. As one of the care attendants said:

> 'If someone wants a salad at 11 o'clock in the morning, that is what she will get. Our cook has no difficulty with these odd requests.'

In one centre the conditions for producing meals are excellent, but in the second they are cramped and overcrowded. In spite of this, the manager of this centre reported:

> 'Our cook is excellent. She produces breakfast, morning tea, cooked lunch and cooked pudding for 25 clients and service providers every day. [The] kitchen is far too small, not enough equipment or room for equipment. She does a great job with little resources.'

6.4.3.2 Hair-care and Baths/Showers

In both dementia-specific day centres, care attendants provide much of the hair-care, as part of the bathing and showering routine. As many of the service providers and family carers repeatedly pointed out, persuading older people with dementia to have a shower, bath, hair wash or a change of clothes can be a difficult and time-consuming exercise. Often, one care attendant may be more successful than others at persuading an older person to have a shower or a bath. In this situation, when an older person with dementia agrees to a hair wash, waiting for the weekly visit from the hairdresser does not make a great deal of sense.

The facilities for hair-care, bathing and showering contrast sharply between the two centres. In one, the facilities are very good; in the other, they are quite unacceptable by any standards. As one of the care attendants described it:

> 'The shower and toilet facilities are dreadful. We have three unisex toilets with a small, tight, communal changing area for all the clients. Incontinence is an issue in a centre like this and at the very least we badly need separate facilities for men and women. It is very, very undignified, and the men in particular find it embarrassing. Holding onto their dignity can be very difficult for these people at the best of times without subjecting them to this.'

6.4.3.3 Nursing

Both dementia-specific day centres are nurse-led, with the general opinion being that this was vitally important in centres for older people with Alzheimer's and other forms of dementia. In one of the centres, the manager herself is the only trained nurse and she badly felt the need for more support. There is no cover for her when she is sick, takes leave or needs to attend a meeting. During

122

consultations with the three care attendants in this centre, they all called for additional nursing support.

6.4.3.4 Transport

One of the centres has transport of its own. As with several other centres, traffic creates difficulties. Some of the older people with dementia could be on the bus for up to two hours which, in the manager's opinion is far too long. The centre has another bus (that at the time was being serviced) but no second driver. The manager is hoping to solve this problem with the result being two bus runs each day and less time spent in the bus as a consequence.

Some older people, especially those with carers who work outside the home, are brought in and collected by private family transport.

6.4.3.5 Chiropody and Physiotherapy

Chiropody is regarded as an essential service by providers in both dementia-specific day centres, but it is only offered in one. The second centre has been unable to offer chiropody since the centre opened five years ago. This is due to a combination of funding difficulties and not being able to find a suitable chiropodist. The care workers are not allowed to cut nails, so the absence of a chiropody service is a difficulty for some of the older people. Physiotherapy is only offered in one of the two centres, funding difficulties again being the reason for this.

6.4.4 Social Activities Provided

The main activities in the two dementia-specific day centres aim to reflect the different needs of these older people. Head, neck and hand massage, and touching and caressing, is calming and relaxing for them. Reminiscence using videos about old skills and traditions, and discussion about their younger days, is very stimulating. Other activities include art therapy, very gentle exercises, listening to old-time music and saying prayers.

Lack of space was a problem for the service providers in both centres, particularly in achieving their social activity goals. One care attendant felt that, although her centre was very imaginative and attentive when providing stimulating social activities, improvements could still be made if there was more space:

'The only negative side is that we do not have enough space … [I] would love to have more space for a bigger garden and for a room where they could do messy, wet, clay activities and it wouldn't matter if it was untidy or messy – a dedicated art/paint/pottery sort of room.'

The second centre experienced similar difficulties:

'A big problem is lack of space generally. We badly need another day room so that when clients get agitated or there is too much noise in the sitting room, [they] could go to another room. As it is, the hallway is used for this purpose but it is dark and not suitable, and used a lot for pacing up and down.'

Difficulties in stimulating older people with dementia were raised by several care attendants in one centre. In this centre, which is understaffed and structurally deficient in a number of important areas, there was an awareness that the social activity programme was not very exciting, particularly for those with early stage dementia. The centre also wanted to be able to provide more active male-centred activities, such as mini-golf or pinball.

The staff here felt that getting a professional occupational therapist to create a programme for individual older people, that they could then follow, would be very beneficial, but unlikely to happen in the foreseeable future. Without a great deal of extra help from outside volunteers, such as their art therapist, the activities were unlikely to improve.

Being able to provide a suitable and safe outdoor space (for wandering, pacing, tactile exploring, fresh air and exercise) is an important resource in a centre for older people with dementia. Both centres have access to gardens, but one is much smaller than it could be. One of the care attendants explained:

'We do have a pretty little enclosed garden, but beyond that there is a lot of open garden which could be used if we only had an electronic gate. As it is, we do not have the staff to monitor the gate and so that part of the garden is out of bounds for safety reasons. This is a real shame. Some of our men, in particular, get very restless and this would help so much to reduce that.'

6.4.5 Respite for Carers

Caring for older people can sometimes be difficult, tiring and stressful. This is especially true for those caring for older people with dementia. The service providers in the dementia-specific day centres are certainly more aware of their responsibilities in supporting and giving respite to family carers. For many of them (and this was a view supported by several PHNs), the lack of weekend support places a real strain on these family carers. Although many of them argued that the older people themselves could not really cope with longer days in care (for some even four to six hours per day is too long), the provision of care at the weekends, even for just a few hours each day, would lift a huge burden from family carers.

6.4.6 Care Plans for Older People

Preparing a considered care plan for each individual older person and consulting with family carers, is an important aspect of day care service, particularly in these centres. Older people with dementia may be vulnerable due to their inability to clearly express their likes and dislikes, their preferences and objections, and their fears and anxieties. It was emphasised that all the service providers, whether nurse managers, care attendants, drivers, visiting professionals or volunteers, should be consulted, involved and informed about the care plan for each older person attending the centres.

6.5 Consultations with PHNs

The three PHNs who were consulted were all very supportive of the two dementia-specific day centres, and the services and resources they provide. However, along with many other PHNs, they were very critical of the general lack of services for older people with dementia. As one put it:

> 'There are not enough facilities for older people with dementia. There are not enough places in day care, the transport situation is appaling and there is nothing for crisis situations. Because of the lack of proper transport, I know of cases where people with Alzheimer's were put into long-term care, even with the support of a home-sitter.'

The problems experienced by carers of older people with advanced dementia presented a particular area of difficulty. For some carers, taking their relatives out of their own homes on a daily basis causes so much trauma and agitation, as well as so much distress to family and other older people, that day care is just not an option. Day care answers the needs of many older people and their family carers, but by no means all. There is a huge need, according to the PHNs, for increased respite care and home-sitting services for older people with more severe or advanced dementia.

6.6 The Primary and Secondary Objectives of Dementia-Specific Day Centres

From these consultations, it is possible to refine the primary and secondary objectives of dementia-specific day centres, as shown in the Preliminary Classification of Day Services in Ireland.

The *primary objectives* of the dementia-specific day centres are:

- to prevent older people from going into long-term care

- to provide protective and appropriate supervision for older people with dementia

- to provide assistance with personal care and health care

- to provide support and respite for carers

- health promotion.

The *secondary objectives* of the dementia-specific day centres are:

- to provide social interaction/social activities

- to facilitate personal development.

6.7 Gaps and Deficits/Challenges

Consultations with service providers and PHNs revealed wide ranging gaps and deficits in the day services intended to support the most vulnerable – older people with dementia and their family carers. Many of these gaps and deficits are directly related to lack of funding. They include:

- insufficient numbers of centres

- understaffing, including lack of cover for nurse managers and the need for more nursing support

- transport

- lack of space; cramped and overcrowded conditions; demeaning personal care facilities

- difficulties in stimulating older people with dementia

- suitable social activity programmes, especially for older men and those with early stage dementia

- longer opening hours and weekend opening to support carers

- difficulties in easing the problems experienced by carers of older people with advanced dementia

- lack of services for crisis situations.

At the beginning of this report it was noted that Irish society is ageing. By 2030, the proportion of the population aged over 65 years will have grown from 11 per cent in the mid-1990s to around 20 per cent. With this growing population of older people, it is estimated that by 2030 more than 55,000 people in Ireland will suffer from dementia, compared with about 33,000 currently (CSO, 2001). This growth will continue to give rise to additional demands for services for older people with dementia.

At present, much of the service provision for this group of older people comes from the voluntary sector. The Alzheimer's Society of Ireland, for example, operates more than twenty dementia-specific day care centres and employs about 350 home care workers. Quality services for older people with special needs, including those with dementia, are expensive in relation to day care for other categories of older people. Current funding for the two voluntary organisations running the dementia-specific day centres featured in this study, covers only sixty per cent of their total budget and is clearly insufficient to meet current levels of need.

Chapter Seven

Consultations in the Social Club

Chapter Seven

Consultations in the Social Club

7.1 Introduction

In order to meet the aims of the study, consultations were carried out in one social club. Table 7.1 shows the numbers of people that were consulted.

Table 7.1: Consultations in the social club

Category	Numbers
Older people attending social club	5
Older people not attending social club	2
Family carers	1
Service providers	4
PHNs	2

7.2 Consultations with Older People Attending the Social Club

This group of people were similar in age to many of those consulted in other centres, but it was apparent that the older people attending the social club were stimulated intellectually, behaviourally and technologically, in ways that the others were not. This does not mean that none of the other centres ever provide similar challenges, simply that none were actually encountered during this study.

These older people clearly revelled in the challenging activities, discussing them with the utmost enthusiasm, and yet nearly every one of these activities demanded commitment, hard work and responsibility on their part.

One example is the Drama Club. It joined with school children from the locality for an intergenerational project that was then performed in Belfast, Derry and the National Concert Hall in Dublin:

> 'I have a ball, especially with the Drama Club. My family is delighted;
> I have great confidence, never suffer from depression or illness even
> though I had a bad heart attack a few years ago.'

> 'I love the Drama Club, I just love it.'

Another example, even more demanding in terms of responsibility and commitment, is the Senior Help Line, which was started by this club some years ago to provide support for older people who feel lonely and isolated. The service is operated on a voluntary basis by the older people themselves, many of whom are well into their eighties.

All the volunteers undergo a specially designed training programme that is supported by other volunteer groups, including the Samaritans. With the ongoing support and help of the health boards, this service has now developed from this centre to become a national service. There are currently about three hundred older people providing the service from eleven centres all over the country. Older people consulted for this study said:

> 'The Senior Help Line is a very useful and necessary service. We get
> insight into how other older people live. I volunteer once every six weeks
> and I love it.'

> 'I'm a Help Line volunteer – very important, the training was excellent.
> This place means everything to me, brilliant, coming for ten years, just
> love everything about it.'

Other activities important to the social club members include their keep fit classes, dancing, trips and outings, picnics and holidays, speech writing, using their resource library, meeting each other in the coffee area, and giving knitting and crochet classes in the local primary school. One older woman spoke for the group when she declared:

> 'Coming here makes life worth living.'

7.3 Consultations with Older People Not Attending

Consultations were carried out with two older women in the community, in their late seventies and early eighties, whom the manager of the centre thought would benefit from becoming members. One lived almost beside the centre. Both were widowed and both lived alone.

As with so many of the older people consulted, these older people were very insistent that they were content to stay at home and did not wish to participate in activities that held no real appeal for them. They did not feel lonely or isolated; both had the support of family and neighbours, and both found great comfort in their faith.

In the view of one person, those older people who used the social club were probably lonely or depressed, or had no support from their families.

7.4 Consultations with Family Carers

The one family carer spoken to in this social club reinforced many of the important points already made by other family carers. She aptly summed up her views of the club:

> 'She is so happy. She loves the outings, the picnics, being a Help Line volunteer at the age of 86. She has been on many holidays – copes with her pains and keeps her from dwelling on them. The centre has made her a woman of the world.'

This social club is fundamentally different from the other centres in the study. Its philosophy is to constantly challenge and push back the classic 'boundaries' of old age by facilitating its ninety members (ranging in age from mid-fifties to mid-nineties) to demonstrate that 'there is no age at which expression of activity and emotions are supposed to cease'. There are numerous examples of this philosophy in action but one in particular is that in 1999, in association with the European Network of Older Volunteers, this social club hosted a European conference in Ireland entitled *Towards Social Inclusion: The Contribution of Older People*. The aim of the conference was to improve knowledge of social exclusion among older people in both urban and rural Europe, and to promote the actions of the Social Club members in combating isolation and exclusion. The conference played host to over 170 delegates from 17 countries and the entire event was organised and run by the members of the social club themselves.

The manager of the centre described the members:

> 'They are never afraid of a challenge, breaking down barriers and giving
> back to the community. They are very enthusiastic about volunteering for
> projects and eager to participate. They are not only extremely active, but
> show an enormous passion for learning and a willingness to help others.'

The service providers believed strongly that the social club confers tangible and measurable health benefits on the older people attending. Apart from their own observations regarding low levels of depression and high levels of physical energy and enthusiasm among the members, the service providers quote the local general practitioner who has noticed a real decline in the surgery attendance of these older people.

Without exception, the physical environment of the social club (in terms of the building structure, the space and other facilities) is by far the poorest of the fifteen centres visited. Several of the service providers commented that the building is difficult to heat in winter and to keep cool in summer. The resource centre has to double as a project office while in-house programmes such as the Women's Health Initiative and keep fit can only cater for a maximum of 35 people, even though there are many more members wishing to join. Service providers and the members themselves look forward to the day when they will have a spacious designated building.

The social club, which is managed by the members and supported by a manager and three project co-ordinators, has no core funding. It gathers its funding from a wide mixture of both voluntary and statutory sources, including fundraising by the members, statutory support for specific projects and lottery funds. For example, in the last few years the club has received a government grant for computer equipment and training, a county council arts grant, a health board grant for remotely monitored alarm systems and a Millennium Recognition Award for a transport project. The club is actively administering a Social Economy project and is hoping to start up a laundry service on a commercial basis.

For the service providers and members of this facility, much of the energy that they would like to donate to their projects and activities is being diverted towards fundraising, which they described as becoming more and more difficult all the time. They speak about operating all the time 'from hand to mouth'.

7.5.1 Social Activities Provided

The range of activities in the social club is very diverse. The ethos here is to not only provide a medium through which the abilities, skills and experiences of the members can find expression, but also to encourage the older people to give something back to the wider community. The members of this group, therefore, are involved not only in the conventional programmes of an active retirement group such as a choir, drama, creative dancing and keep fit, but also in community projects. For instance, they operate the Senior Help Line, the mentoring programme for adult students in out-reach education and also a knitting tuition programme in local primary schools. All these activities give something back to the community and show a willingness to help others.

Part of the activity programme involves linking up with other national and international organisations, including the National Senior Citizens Parliament, similar organisations in France, Italy, Spain, and Finland, the European Network of Older Volunteers and various committees at EU level. As one of the project managers explained:

> 'We nourish independence, choice and responsibility. Our members are encouraged in public policy and issue press releases on policy documents. We have a strong democratic element with full discussion on everything.'

7.5.2 Projects

At any one time, with the support of project co-ordinators, the members of the social club are running a number of different projects. One current project has been funded under the Department of Enterprise's CAIT (Community Application of Information Technology) programme. This programme was introduced, in association with the Information Society Commission, to encourage 'late adopters' such as older people, to use and become familiar with new technologies in their everyday lives. The project co-ordinators report that the members have embraced this project with enormous enthusiasm.

Through a number of different project strands, including their intergenerational schools project (which involves working with local primary school children) and their 'mentoring scheme' (with adult students in out-reach programmes), the older members of this social club are successfully mastering the skills of word processing, spreadsheets, the Internet and e-mailing, and the techniques involved in creating graphics for presentations and reports, as well as the use of scanners, digital cameras and web-cams.

7.5.3 Transport

In common with several other service providers, the manager of the social club described lack of transport in rural areas as a huge problem. For some time, the members of the club were very aware that older people in the community were unable to attend the club simply through lack of appropriate transport. And so they formed a fundraising committee whose purpose was to purchase a 16-seater minibus with a hydraulic lift and capacity for three wheelchairs. For this club, with such an active programme, having its own transport is essential.

7.5.4 Personal Care (Hair-care, Baths/Showers, Chiropody)

The social club does not offer a hairdressing service at present. The manager hopes to consider it, if and when more space is available. At the moment it is not regarded as a priority service, either by the service providers or the members of the club who were consulted for this study.

The club does offer some care services – a chiropodist visits one day a month and the service is always heavily booked – and it is actively planning a laundry service. The service providers would consider offering physiotherapy if more space were available but not a shower/bath service. There is currently no demand for this service and this was confirmed during consultations with the members.

7.6 Consultations with PHNs

Perhaps because this centre is principally an active social club, with very little of the caring service as understood and offered in the other centres, the two PHNs consulted here were actually visiting for the first time. Everybody involved in the study agreed that the low demand for traditional caring services was an excellent endorsement of the social club's policies.

7.7 The Primary and Secondary Objectives of the Social Club

From these consultations, it is possible to refine the primary and secondary objectives of social clubs, as shown in the Preliminary Classification of Day Services in Ireland.

The *primary objectives* of the social club are:

- to prevent older people from going into long-term care

- to facilitate social interaction/social activities

- to facilitate personal development

- to facilitate empowerment

- health promotion

- to encourage integration in the community.

The *secondary objectives* of the social club are:

- to encourage further and lifelong education

- to provide health, social care and welfare services information.

These objectives, and the structural and process components of service delivery required to achieve these objectives, will be further discussed in Chapter Eight.

7.8 Gaps and Deficits/Challenges

There is no doubt that this social club, through its philosophy of challenging the boundaries of old age, the involvement of all its members in all aspects of its programmes of activities, projects and courses, and the respect and regard that members and staff have for each other reaps considerable physical, social, and emotional rewards. As with all the other models there were gaps and deficits in the service, principally:

- lack of core funding

- an unsuitable building with poor infrastructure.

This club, as with other social clubs, active retirement groups and senior citizens' clubs, has no secure funding. It gathers its funding from a mixture of voluntary and statutory sources, including fundraising, occasional statutory grants for specific projects and lottery funding. The project co-ordinators and club members spend a great deal of time fundraising and making grant applications. The uncertainties of funding mean that planning for development and growth is not an easy task.

Chapter Eight

Structural and Process Components of Service Delivery

Chapter Eight

Structural and Process Components of Service Delivery

8.1 Introduction

In order to inform this study, the Consultative Committee convened to oversee the research drew up a Preliminary Classification of Day Services in Ireland (Table 1.1). On the basis of the consultations carried out for the study, it became apparent that the service objectives for the different models of day services, as detailed in the Preliminary Classification of Day Services in Ireland, required substantial revision.

8.2 Revised Classification of Day Services in Ireland

The Revised Classification of Day Services in Ireland (Table 8.1) shows the revised primary and secondary objectives for each of four defined models, as well as reviewing the staffing, management, selection and funding classifications. However, it must be borne in mind that for a variety of historical, infrastructural, geographical and practical reasons, there are, and will continue to be, facilities that straddle two and possibly three of these models.

8.2.1 Issues of Clarification

The research process began with the identification of four models of day service provision, on the basis of best evidence from the Consultative Committee with regard to the different types of facility that exist 'on the ground'. However, the research demonstrated that in practice only two of the facilities described in the Preliminary Classification of Day Services in Ireland exist as they were originally described.

In the Preliminary Classification of Day Services in Ireland, day care centres were classified as being under the direction of the health boards and entirely health board-funded. Day centres were separately classified as being under their own direction. It is clear from the consultations, however, that the term 'day care centre' should be used not only for those facilities that are under the direction of and funded by the health boards, but also those voluntary sector 'day centres' that are under their own direction and either fully or partially funded by the health board, and have other aspects, such as service objectives, in common with day care centres.

According to the Revised Classification of Day Services in Ireland, if a centre meets the criteria set out for day care centres, it is classified as such, whether it is managed by a health board or a voluntary agency, or whether it is fully health board-funded or funded by a health board/voluntary agency partnership.

This report describes a number of 'mixed' centres that were classed as day care centres/social clubs because they straddled the day care centre and the social centre as described in the Preliminary Classification. These centres, which were located towards the 'social model' end of the care spectrum, now fall into the Revised Classification of Day Services in Ireland category of social club/day centre. This descriptor has been used because it is the term adopted by the National Working Group on Performance Indicators.

Unlike many day care centres, social club/day centres are usually health board-funded in part, with any remaining funding coming from service charges, fundraising and other agencies such as FÁS. They are generally managed by a voluntary agency and they have an open selection membership.

It is important to note that while the Revised Classification of Day Services in Ireland refers to different emphases in the primary and secondary objectives for these two models, there are some centres which are primarily day care centres that provide services to more active older people, just as there are some centres which are primarily social club/day centres that provide services to more dependent older people.

Table 8.1: Revised classification of day services in Ireland

Facility	Primary objectives	Secondary objectives	Staff	Management or direction	Selection	Funding
Day care centre* (Day care service)	To prevent older people from going into long-term care To support independent living among older people To provide assistance with personal care and health care To facilitate activation/ social interaction To provide support and respite for carers To provide a forum for health promotion	To assist in the maintenance of function To provide health, social care and welfare services information To facilitate personal development To provide individual services at a personal level	Health care professionals +/- multi-disciplinary team or part thereof	Under direction of health board or voluntary agencies	Referral from PHN, GP, community care and hospital in-patients discharged from Care of the Elderly teams	Health board funded or partially health board funded, service charges

* Some centres that are primarily day care centres also provide services to more active older people.

Table 8.1: Revised classification of day services in Ireland (continued)

Facility	Primary objectives	Secondary objectives	Staff	Management or direction	Selection	Funding
Social club/day centre** (Social satellite centre)	To prevent older people from going into long-term care To facilitate social interaction/social activities To encourage personal development To provide a forum for health promotion	To provide minor personal care To provide health, social care and welfare services information To support and provide respite for carers To provide individual services at a personal level	Health care professionals/ volunteers/local council/voluntary group or religious community	Under own direction	Open selection: membership defined by themselves	Partially health board funded plus service charges, fundraising, funding from other agencies e.g. FÁS

** Some centres that are primarily social clubs/day centres also provide services to more dependent older people.

Table 8.1: Revised classification of day services in Ireland (continued)

Facility	Primary objectives	Secondary objectives	Staff	Management or direction	Selection	Funding
Social club (Senior citizens' club or active retirement group)	To prevent older people from going into long-term care To facilitate social interaction/social activities To facilitate personal development To facilitate empowerment To provide a forum for health promotion To encourage integration in the community	To encourage further and lifelong education To provide health, social care and welfare services information	Volunteers and members	Under own direction	Open selection: membership	No core funding from health board, fundraising, private sponsorship, service charges, grant applications to health board and other agencies

Table 8.1: Revised classification of day services in Ireland (continued)

Facility	Primary objectives	Secondary objectives	Staff	Management or direction	Selection	Funding
Dementia-specific day centre (Alzheimer's centre)	To prevent older people from going into long-term care To provide protective and appropriate supervision for older people with dementia To provide assistance with personal care and health care To provide support and respite for carers To provide a forum for health promotion	To provide opportunities for social interaction/social activities To facilitate personal development	Health care professionals +/- nursing/physiotherapy Volunteers	Direction of Alzheimer's Society/Western Alzheimer Foundation or similar	Open selection: membership decided by centre	Partial health board funding, service charges, fundraising, grant applications to health board and other agencies

As discussed in Chapter One, *The Years Ahead* (1988) report defined the main purposes of day centres, but did not develop service objectives in such a way as to give meaningful direction to service operations and development. Convery (1987) argued that a major weakness in the community care system as a whole has been that service objectives, including those for day services for older people, have not been adequately developed. The Health Strategy *Quality and Fairness* (Department of Health and Children, 2001) also noted this weakness. In its review of services for older people in a policy context, it has set out as one of its high performance goals, the preparation of national standards for community and long-term residential care for older people.

The Revised Classification of Day Services in Ireland shows revised primary and secondary objectives for each of four defined models, in addition to refined staffing, management, selection and funding classifications. In order to give positive direction to service development, it was also decided to detail the components of service delivery that would be required to achieve such service objectives in the different facilities. This analysis was informed by feedback from service providers, who identified services and standards of service delivery that they felt were necessary to achieve their objectives. The Consultative Committee also proposed that providing such details would facilitate evaluation processes by acting as a checklist against which current service provision could be measured. To this end, an analytical approach originally proposed by Donabedian (1966; 1988) (an early pioneer and a seminal influence in the areas of measuring quality of care), was used in this study. Donabedian's work, which was referred to in some detail by Delaney *et al.* (2001), focuses on three main aspects of service delivery: structure, process and outcome. In using such an approach, the research proposes that if the structural and process components of service delivery are in place, as described in the report, then day services should achieve their service objectives or desired outcomes.

8.3.1 Structural Components of Service Delivery

The term 'structural components of service delivery' refers to the organisational framework of the programme and the components that contribute to it. In the context of the consultative findings of this study, this would include the integral components that constitute it. These are:

- funding and its level of security – this has direct implications for the level and standard of the service provided in all types of facilities

- staffing – certain staffing requirements are necessary in order to meet the varying health care, social care and dependency needs of older people attending the various facilities

- level of service provision – a quality standard and level of service provision is required in order to meet the varying health care, social care and dependency needs of older people attending the various facilities

- services provided – an appropriate range of services must be provided.

8.3.2 Process Components of Service Delivery

Process refers to how the structures function. The process aspect considers the way in which services are provided and would, in the context of this study, include:

- the ethos, values and principles which direct and inform the service

- process of care delivery

- involvement of older people and their carers.

From the comprehensive consultations carried out for this study and the expert input of the Consultative Committee, the structural and process components of service delivery that must be met in order to fulfil the primary and secondary objectives presented in the Revised Classification of Day Services in Ireland, can be defined.

The following tables present the structural and process components for each of the four models: day care centres; social club/day centres; dementia-specific day centres; and social clubs.

Table 8.2: Structural components of service delivery

DCC: Day care centre   **DSDC:** Dementia-specific day centre

SC/DC: Social club/day centre   **SC:** Social club

Structure	Quality Components	DCC	SC/DC	DSDC	SC
Funding	Facilities, whether under the direction of the health board, a voluntary agency or a partnership of both, should have the funding needed to: ● achieve stated service objectives ● provide evidence of needs assessment having been carried out ● employ sufficient numbers and types of staff ● offer sufficient and appropriate services ● cater for clients' needs.	X	X	X	X
	Service charges to older people and/or their carers should be standardised.	X	X	X	
	Social clubs should have secure core funding and be considered as an equal component in the continuum of day services.				X
Staffing: numbers	The resources should be available to provide sufficient numbers of staff, at all levels, to meet the needs of the members.	X	X	X	X
	Relief or back-up staff should be available when needed.	X	X	X	X

Table 8.2: Structural components of service delivery (continued)

Structure	Quality Components	DCC	SC/DC	DSDC	SC
Staffing: qualifications	All staff should be appropriately qualified.	x	x	x	x
	Services should be led by a professional with appropriate experience/interest in older people.	x	x	x	x
	Ongoing training for all staff and volunteers, both part-time and full-time, should be encouraged.	x	x	x	x
	There should be access to a qualified nurse.	x			
	Service should be nurse-led.			x	
	All staff should be appropriately qualified, with an excellent understanding of the needs and vulnerabilities of older people with dementia.			x	
Level of service provision	Facilities should be open seven days a week, all year round, with flexible opening hours.	x	x	x	x
	In order to accommodate carers who work, the facility should be open from 8am to 6pm.	x		x	
	Older people attending should have equal access based on their needs.	x	x	x	
	There should be appropriate funding, staffing and space to ensure that there are no long waiting lists or overcrowding.	x	x	x	
	All older people should have access to a service appropriate to their needs, abilities and preferences.	x	x	x	x

Table 8.2: Structural components of service delivery (continued)

Structure	Quality Components	DCC	SC/DC	DSDC	SC
Level of service provision (continued)	Social clubs and social club/day centres should: ● be flexible in their opening hours and reflect the wishes of the older members ● welcome all older people ● act as a base from which older people can provide for the needs of each other ● act as a base from which older people can reach out to the wider world.		x		x
Referral to day services	There should be effective referral mechanisms that take account of the older person's perspectives and personal goals.	x	x	x	
	For more active older people, referral should be flexible, with an emphasis on self-referral.	x	x		x
	When an older person is on a waiting list the PHN should be in regular contact until a place has been found.	x		x	
Referral to outside services	Day services should be linked to all relevant providers of services for older people (whether community- or hospital-based) including: ● physiotherapists ● chiropodists ● occupational therapists ● ophthalmologists ● dieticians ● social workers ● pharmacists.	x	x	x	

Table 8.2: Structural components of service delivery (continued)

Structure	Quality Components	DCC	SC/DC	DSDC	SC
Building	Services and activities should be delivered in buildings that: • conform to the highest standards • are bright, spacious and appropriately furnished • are completely accessible in all aspects of disability • provide a safe and healthy environment for users, visitors and staff • have two day-rooms – one for quiet activities and one for group/noisy activities.	x	x	x	x
Transport	Facilities should have: • centre-controlled transport with sufficient seating, a ramp, hoist and wheelchair capacity • a qualified driver with first aid and resuscitation qualifications • a care attendant to accompany the driver at all times on health and safety grounds.	x	x	x	x
	Older people should not have to spend excessive time travelling to the service.	x	x	x	x
Midday meals	Facilities should: • provide a nutritious well-balanced meal prepared in a clean, hygienic kitchen which meets health and safety regulations • provide a choice of midday meal, where possible.	x	x	x	

Table 8.2: Structural components of service delivery (continued)

Structure	Quality Components	DCC	SC/DC	DSDC	SC
Personal care (bath/ showers, hair-care)	Facilities should have: • showers/bathroom that are capable of accommodating two people as well as the older person, and should have a toilet and a washbasin • appropriate facilities for showering, bathing and hair-care in safety, dignity and comfort.	X	X	X	
	Facilities should have appropriate single sex toilets.	X	X	X	X
Nursing	A professional nursing service, which is co-ordinated and linked to a community, multi-disciplinary team, should be available.	X		X	
	Service may be nurse-led depending on the mix of older people attending.	X	X	X	
Chiropody	There should be a quality chiropody service with appropriate facilities and space, delivered by a qualified chiropodist with sufficient frequency and regularity to meet the needs of the older people attending.	X	X	X	
	Where this is not possible, adequate referral procedures should be in place for outside visits to these practitioners.	X	X	X	
Physiotherapy	There should be a quality physiotherapy service, with appropriate facilities and space, based on an accurate assessment of the requirements of the older person (whether medical or health promoting).	X	X	X	

Table 8.2: Structural components of service delivery (continued)

Structure	Quality Components	DCC	SC/DC	DSDC	SC
Physiotherapy (continued)	This service should be delivered by a qualified physiotherapist with sufficient frequency and regularity to meet the needs of the older people attending.	x	x	x	
	Where this is not possible, adequate referral mechanisms should be in place for outside visits to these practitioners.	x	x	x	
Occupational therapy	There should be a quality occupational therapy service, with appropriate facilities and space, based on an accurate assessment of the requirements of the older person.	x	x	x	
	This service should be delivered by a qualified occupational therapist with sufficient frequency and regularity to meet the needs of the older people attending.	x	x	x	
	Where this is not possible, adequate referral mechanisms should be in place for outside visits to these practitioners.	x	x	x	
Social activities	The facility should have a flexible and varied social activities programme which: • is established in consultation with older people themselves • promotes choice • promotes social contact and social stimulation appropriate to the needs, abilities and preferences of the older people attending.	x	x	x	x

Structure	Quality Components	DCC	SC/DC	DSDC	SC
Social activities (continued)	There should be a social activities co-ordinator or, at the minimum, sufficient staff to engage meaningfully in social activities with older people.	x	x		x
	Social activities programmes should be sufficiently varied to appeal to a wide range of needs, abilities and preferences.	x	x	x	x
	Activities should include those that are challenging in terms of learning new skills and tasks, and promoting self development.	x	x		x
	Activities should encourage socially inclusive interactions with the wider community.	x	x	x	x
	There should be a co-ordinator of social activities trained in the special needs of older people with dementia.	x		x	
	The programme of social activities should: • challenge older people to constantly push back the boundaries in everything they do • encourage lifelong learning • promote community and intergenerational solidarity.				x

Table 8.3: Process components of service delivery

Process	Quality components	DCC	SC/DC	DSDC	SC
Ethos, values and principles of day service provision	Services should be person-centred and support older people in retaining as much autonomy and control over their lives as possible.	X	X	X	X
	Access to the service should be equitable and based on need.	X	X	X	X
	Services should promote a positive image of ageing within and outside the centre.	X	X	X	X
	Services should be: ● needs focused ● abilities focused ● user-driven ● empowering ● motivating.	X	X	X	X
	Services should meet the needs, requirements and wishes of older people through: ● social care and company ● activation and maintenance ● assessment and monitoring.	X	X	X	
	Through the ethos, values and principles of the services provided, older people should: ● feel respected and cherished ● feel encouraged to maintain a sense of identity, dignity and independence ● be able to exercise choice and control in deciding their own needs, wants and goals.	X	X	X	X

Table 8.3: Process components of service delivery (continued)

Process	Quality components	DCC	SC/DC	DSDC	SC
Ethos, values and principles of day service provision (continued)	Through the ethos, values and principles of the services provided, family carers should: • have complete confidence in the ability of the service to treat their loved ones with gentleness and respect, in a safe environment • feel valued and supported in their role as family carer.	X	X	X	X
	Older people should be supported in maintaining and, where possible, improving their physical, emotional and psychological health and quality of life.	X	X	X	X
	Services should reflect the special needs and vulnerabilities of older people with dementia.	X		X	
	Social clubs and social clubs/day centres should: • provide a medium through which the abilities, skills and experiences of the members can find expression • develop a more holistic response to the needs of older people • interface with the local community • harness, stimulate and continue to revitalise the resources that older people present.		X		X

Table 8.3: Process components of service delivery (continued)

Process	Quality components	DCC	SC/DC	DSDC	SC
Process of care delivery	Services should be delivered in an environment of respect and care, gentleness and friendliness.	x	x	x	x
	Services should be delivered by committed, caring and flexible staff who will: ● encourage maintenance and activation ● have time to talk and listen to older people ● be a source of companionship, social stimulation and motivation ● encourage empowerment of older people through interaction with them ● provide relief and support for carers ● identify older people who may be being abused.	x	x	x	x
	Services should raise the profile of the facility within the community by promoting: ● community-wide activities ● volunteering.	x	x	x	x
	The needs of older people with dementia should be assessed regularly.	x		x	
	The frequency of visits to the centres should be based on need and not other considerations such as space or transport availability.	x	x	x	x
	Consultation should be carried out directly with older men to consider their special requirements regarding appropriate services and activities.	x	x	x	x

Table 8.3: Process components of service delivery (continued)

Process	Quality components	DCC	SC/DC	DSDC	SC
Involvement of older people and family carers	Services should involve older people and/or their carers in the assessment process, which should be broad based and take account of interests and abilities as well as physical and mental status.	x	x	x	
	At all times there should be an awareness of the special needs of those caring for older people with dementia, especially when the carers themselves are older people.	x		x	
	Pathways of care for each older person should be drawn up in consultation with the older person and the family carer, and reviewed regularly.	x	x	x	
	There should be a complaints mechanism in place for older people and their carers.	x	x	x	x
	Regular consultations should be carried out with the older members to ensure that the service is appropriate to their requirements.	x	x	x	x
	At all levels of service provision, older people should be able to exercise choice and control in deciding their own needs, wants and goals.	x	x	x	x

Evaluation can take many different forms. Delaney *et al.* (2001) proposes that it is most effective to conceptualise evaluation efforts along a continuum with three main types emerging, reflecting the three main components of service delivery: structure, process and outcome. These are descriptive evaluations, which describe the service's main structural components; programme review evaluations, which review the quality of a service's practice; and impact evaluations, which measure the effects of service delivery (Table 8.4).

Table 8.4: Structure, process and outcome-based evaluations

When evaluating	Structural components	Process components	Outcomes/ desired objectives
Evaluation approach	Descriptive evaluation	Programme review evaluation	Impact evaluation

8.4.1 Descriptive Evaluations

Descriptive evaluations are perhaps the most fundamental in the evaluation continuum. The development of services and practice will be contingent, to some extent, on what is actually happening with regard to the structural components of service delivery. Those funding services or programmes often find descriptive accounts useful for demonstrating whether resources have been used as agreed, and as a mechanism for monitoring expenditure (McCartney, 1992).

Although descriptive evaluation often involves collecting and recording quantitative data (e.g. how many bus journeys are made, how many older people travel by bus and how much this transport service costs), it also involves collecting and monitoring 'softer' information about the nature of structural variables. Examples of this would be describing the types of services being delivered, how they are organised and the categories of older people in receipt of the service.

As Delaney *et al.* (2001) point outs, developing key indicators for a descriptive evaluation can be relatively straightforward if the service organisation already routinely collects and records the information needed to describe structural variables. However, while descriptive evaluation seems superficially straightforward, there may be problems in practice. It can determine whether a service was offered, but it does not give any insight into whether it was worth offering. It can compile an inventory of services and activities, but may inadequately describe the commitment and enthusiasm that went into providing them. Or alternatively, may give those services and activities a status which they do not deserve.

For these reasons, as reported in Delaney *et al.* (2001), descriptive evaluation efforts can effectively document and describe the structure of a service, but they do not by themselves indicate the effectiveness of the entirety of the service. They do, however, provide a good basis for the other types of evaluations, namely, programme review evaluations and impact evaluations.

8.4.2 Programme Review Evaluations

Programme review evaluations of process of care variables are directed towards fully understanding how a service works and how it produces that results that it does. There are an unlimited number of questions that might be asked in such evaluations. For this reason, questions must be selected by carefully considering what it is important to know about, for example, developmental aspects of service, quality of service and appropriateness of service.

Each of these areas alone could generate numerous questions to render the evaluation exercise non-viable. Examples of questions that may be asked when designing an evaluation to understand and/or closely examine the service processes include:

- on what basis do service providers and/or older people decide which services are needed?

- what do service providers and/or older people consider to be the strengths and/or weaknesses of this service?

- do service providers and/or older people have any complaints about this service and, if so, how are they dealt with?

8.4.3 Impact Evaluations

An impact evaluation assesses the service in terms of achievement of objectives. It could ask, for example, whether there are measurable and demonstrable health and social benefits for older people attending day services. An outcomes-based evaluation asks if the service being provided affects the people it serves differently than an alternative model or an older model of the existing service would.

Delaney *et al.* (2001) argues that undertaking impact evaluation can be difficult and very demanding on resources. Designing an effective impact evaluation can require both considerable planning and research capability. Its implementation can require great commitment, time and effort from service providers.

8.4.4 Other Points to be Considered

Before applying these evaluation methods there are three other points to be considered:

- prioritising the components of service delivery to be evaluated

- methodologies used in evaluating services

- who will undertake the evaluation.

8.4.4.1 Prioritising the Components of Service Delivery to be Evaluated

This chapter describes in some detail the structural and process components of service delivery for different types of day services. Regardless of what type of evaluation model is involved, it may not be feasible to evaluate all of these aspects of service delivery. It may be, for example, that only three of four services provided can be evaluated, rather than all the services offered by the given centre. Time and resources are always limited so centres will, within each of the service categories, prioritise and select the three or four most important service components for initial examination.

8.4.4.2 Methodologies Used in Evaluating Services

Numerous methodologies can be used in evaluating various aspects of service provision, depending on the overall purpose. These include questionnaires, interviews, observation, documentation review, focus groups and case studies. If the overall purpose is to quickly and/or easily obtain lots of information from people in a non-threatening way, then a structured questionnaire might be used. If the purpose is to gather accurate information about how a programme actually operates, and processes in particular, then one might use an observation approach. As Table 8.5 (adopted and modified from McNamara, 1999) demonstrates, each methodology, as well as having its specific role, has its advantages and disadvantages.

Table 8.5: Characteristics of methodologies

Method	Overall purpose	Advantages	Disadvantages
Questionnaires surveys, checklists	To quickly and/or easily obtain lots of information from people in a non threatening way	• Can be completed anonymously • Inexpensive to administer • Easy to compare and analyse • Administered to many people	• May not provide careful feedback • Wording can bias a client's responses • Impersonal • Do not give the full story • Can be difficult for older people with e.g. reading/literacy problems
Interviews	To fully understand someone's impressions or experiences	• Obtains a full range and depth of information • Can be flexible with client	• Can be difficult to analyse and compare • Can be costly • Interviewer can bias a client's responses
Documentation review	When an impression of how a programme operates without interrupting the programme is required	• Obtains comprehensive and historical information • No interruption to programme or client's routine in programme • Information already exists • Few biases about information	• Can be time-consuming • Information may be incomplete • Aims may be unclear • Data restricted to that already in existence

Adapted from *Basic Guide to Program Evaluation* (McNamara, 1999)

The final question to consider is who will undertake the evaluation. Delaney *et al.* (2001) points out that when considering any programme of evaluation, the question of who should participate in the process is often one of the last to be considered. A successful evaluation process needs to be based on developing a partnership between all concerned parties. This includes users of services, their carers, service providers and funding bodies, whether these be statutory, voluntary or a combination of both.

Table 8.6: Evaluating structural components

Components	Who will evaluate
Funding	Service providers Funding bodies
Staffing	Service providers Funding bodies
Level of service provision	Service providers Older people/family carers
Services provided	Service providers Older people/family carers

Table 8.7: Evaluating process components

Service objectives	Who will evaluate
Ethos, values and principles of service	Service providers Older people/family carers
Process of care delivery	Service providers Older people/family carers
Involvement of older people and family carers	Service providers Older people/family carers

Chapter Nine

Future Development of Day Services for Older People

165

Chapter Nine

Future Development of Day Services for Older People

9.1 Introduction

Providing a range of day services to support older people who wish to continue living at home in dignity and independence, is a central principle of health policy for older people in Ireland. Numerous studies, in Ireland and elsewhere, have reported that day services confer health, social and psychological benefits on older people (McAvoy, 2001).

This study is the first to consult not only with day service providers but also, in some detail, with older people themselves and their family carers, in order to consider the development of service objectives and the components of service delivery needed to fulfil these objectives. It finds that day services are hugely beneficial to the many different categories of older people attending a variety of day service environments. The services that these centres provide make a demonstrable contribution towards enabling older people to remain in their own homes, either alone or with their families, and to avoid the unwanted and costly alternative of long-term institutional care. The combination of individual services given at a personal level, the nursing and therapeutic services provided directly in the centres or accessed through them, and the social activity and stimulation programmes offered in the day service facilities, is fundamentally important to these older people and their carers.

Apart from the tangible health and social benefits conferred by the delivery of services in all categories of centres, these older people and their family carers become part of a wider network of caring. They are known to, and looked out for by, not only a range of service providers (e.g. members of voluntary committees, managers, care attendants, drivers and volunteers), but also by each other. The social capital gains achieved through mutual support, co-operation, empathy and trust are very real.

There are, however, numerous gaps, deficits and weaknesses which all too often turn what should be a quality service for older people who need and request it, into one with the resources to provide a good quality service for those older people fortunate enough to live in the right area or for those with access to the necessary transport. Alternatively, the service becomes one that does not have adequate resources and functions as best it can under these circumstances.

Many of the gaps, deficits and weaknesses were well known prior to this study being carried out. The NCAOP noted in *The Years Ahead Report: A Review of the Implementation of its Recommendations* (Ruddle *et al.*, 1997) that day care centres seemed to be low on the priority list of health authorities and were provided on a discretionary basis. It further noted that the number of places was well below what was needed and that it varied significantly across the country. The report also observed that the health authorities were relying heavily on the efforts of the voluntary sector for the provision of such services.

In the area of dementia, the Council noted that most older people with dementia lived at home and were looked after by their families, which often placed a heavy burden on the carer. It observed that there was a particular need for additional day care units for older people with dementia, where services such as chiropody, hair-care, bathing and, most importantly, occupational therapy would be available.

The Council further observed, following the findings of Ruddle *et al.* (1997), that transport to and from day care centres remained poor, especially in rural areas. In the Council's opinion, there seemed to be little urgency among health board programme managers and government departments to resolve this problem, despite a widespread agreement that transport presented a serious challenge. With regard to the range of services provided in day care centres, the Council commented that this varied significantly across the country.

Improvements do appear to have been made in these two areas. Extra resources have been made available for transport. With regard to significant variations in the range of services provided, this would appear (from the findings of this study) to be less of an issue. The services provided, certainly in day care centres, social club/day centres and dementia-specific day centres, show many similarities.

Where there were differences in services, they were often due to external and, in some cases short-term, difficulties such as replacing a physiotherapist or chiropodist who has left or a lack of space. These difficulties often led to variations in the delivery of services. Some of these issues are examined for each model of facility.

9.2 Developmental Issues in Day Care Centres

During the consultations undertaken for this study, a number of issues were identified which need to be addressed when considering future development. They are as follows:

- throughout the country, there are insufficient numbers of day care centres resulting in long waiting lists

- day care centres may not be suitable for certain categories of older people such as those with dementia, 'younger' older people with physical disabilities and those older people who no longer require a high level of support through activation and maintenance but have come to rely on the social supports provided

- there are problems with understaffing and anxieties about continuing staffing levels, resulting in difficulties in meeting many of the service objectives

- some day care centres have difficulties in providing certain essential services, particularly physiotherapy

- in the opinions of some service providers, PHNs and older people not attending, motivational issues are sometimes apparent among some of the older people attending day care centres

- many service providers, PHNs and older men themselves report a reluctance among men to attend day care centres

- family carers of older people need greater support, through longer opening hours at the centres and the introduction of weekend opening.

9.2.1 Insufficient Numbers of Day Care Centres

The finding that there are insufficient numbers of day care centres throughout the country, resulting in long waiting lists, is neither new nor surprising. *The Years Ahead* (Department of Health, 1988) recommended that the ratio of day care centres should be one per 1,800 older people. In today's figures this would mean a total of 240 day care centres are needed (see Chapter One).

There is an acute shortage of day care centres throughout the country. In the *Review of the Implementation of the Ten Year Action Plan for Services for Older People 1999-2008* (Eastern Regional Health Authority, 2001), the ERHA estimates that there are currently only 2,000 day care places available in its region, and that in reality many of these 'places' are only available a couple of days a week. It confirms that there is a serious deficit of day care services in parts of the region, with some substantial areas having no service at. In the northern half of one county there are no statutory or voluntary day care services at all.

The same review points out that in some areas the day hospital is supplementing the absence of appropriate day care facilities. All agencies participating in this review considered the value of appropriate day care and respite services within their environs to be fundamental in maintaining older people in their own homes.

An ongoing review of day care services in the Midland Health Board area shows, as in the EHRA, great variations in access. The review predicts that unless the patterns of access begin to change very soon, within the next few years the numbers of day care places projected for those over 75 years will vary from as high as 1:21 older people in some sectors to as low as 1:89 in others.

9.2.2 Unsuitability of Day Care Centres for Certain Categories of Older People

In this study, several service providers and PHNs discussed the unsuitability of day care centres for certain categories of older people (a situation which, in turn, is adding to long waiting lists). These included people with dementia and 'younger' older people with physical disabilities or mobility difficulties often brought about by a serious accident or a chronic long-term condition such as multiple sclerosis.

The issue of older people attending day care centres when they no longer need support through activation and maintenance, but have come to rely on the social supports is a serious and difficult one to address. The managers and PHNs recognise that this need, combined with a shortage of places, means that other older people who do need a high level of support are not receiving it. Without this support they may have to leave their own homes and communities, and enter long-term institutional care.

The centre managers, however, are reluctant to deny the benefits of companionship and social stimulation to those older people who no longer need to attend for other reasons. These older people do not want to leave the day care centres and the service providers do not want to move them on.

One of the service providers proposed a solution to this difficulty by calling for two different centres – one offering high levels of support and one offering more social activities for those no longer requiring support but wanting companionship. One of the voluntary-run social club/day centres visited during this study provides a very good example of this type of model.

This centre is quite different from all the other facilities visited (see Chapter Five). Here, unlike the other five social club/day centres where the mix of older people is not planned but rather a response to local needs as dictated by local circumstances (such as a lack of transport or more suitable facilities), this centre sets out to serve older people with a range of health and social needs through a philosophy of social inclusion and integration.

The services, programmes and activities available at this particular centre are directed primarily towards older people (and often managed and directed by them) but are not used exclusively by them. This centre has set out to welcome low, medium and high dependency older people, and those needing no care at all.

Its programme of activities, which are sometimes organised according to different abilities and needs, enables older people to move seamlessly between lower and higher levels of support, maintenance and rehabilitation in one location, in the company of the same personnel and, most importantly of all, with the same network of friends and acquaintances.

9.2.3 Understaffing

The problem of understaffing is affecting health and social care services throughout the country but there is a perception among service providers and PHNs that maintaining satisfactory staffing levels in day care centres for older people is not a high priority for health authorities.

Many of the service providers and care attendants reported feeling rushed and hurried, with insufficient time to give to the older people. They reported problems providing cover for staff who were sick and a reliance, in some cases, on older women volunteers from the community to provide a quality service.

Service providers and care attendants are under pressure to perform a certain number of physically demanding and strenuous tasks every day, such as bathing, showering and personal care for older people, preparing and serving meals, cleaning and running activity programmes. Without sufficient numbers of staff, other equally important activities, such as talking with and listening to older people, are neglected.

9.2.4 Difficulties in Providing Certain Essential Services

The services provided by day care centres, and also social club/day centres and dementia-specific day centres, were found to be very similar. These included transport, meals, personal care (showers, baths, hair-care and chiropody) and, quite often, physiotherapy. The physiotherapy service was undoubtedly the most problematical.

Ruddle *et al.* (1997) reported that a physiotherapy service for older people should be developed through the community physiotherapy service operating from health centres, day care centres and social centres. However, at the time of reporting, this development was greatly hampered by the inadequate transport available to deliver older people to the centres.

Since then, the transport services to these facilities have improved. But the older people who are allocated a place in a day care centre and the transport to take them there, are still often deprived of an essential physiotherapy service. This is due to the low numbers of physiotherapy posts offered in community care and the difficulties in recruiting physiotherapists for health board positions.

The current situation regarding physiotherapy, as reported by the service providers, PHNs and older people themselves, seems to be deteriorating. Several reported that physiotherapy services had been discontinued and described making representations to the health boards, but to no avail. This is a service deficit that urgently needs to be addressed.

Lack of sufficient funding for professional services for older people in the community, including physiotherapy, is a phenomenon that has been well documented (Ruddle *et al.*, 1997; Bacon, 2001). It has also been acknowledged, though somewhat obliquely, in the Health Strategy *Quality and Fairness* (2001) in the context of gaps in service provision.

9.2.5 Issues of Motivation

The issue of motivation, which was raised during the consultations, was regarded as a problem by some people but not by others. Day care centres, not surprisingly, reflect the demography of old age and, therefore, are dominated by older women. The social activities in day care centres tend to reflect the interests of the older women attending them.

This study shows that the majority of older people attending day care centres find that the most important part of their day is the enjoyment of peer company through social interaction. The older people feel that their day has a purpose – they are doing something constructive by forming and forging social bonds, learning about one other, and developing new friendships and social networks.

Many service providers and PHNs interpret this as a lack of motivation. Even though the older people report being very happy with what they get at the day care centres, many of the service providers and PHNs feel that it is important to challenge ageist assumptions, held very often by the older people themselves, about what older people want and do not want, or can and cannot do.

9.2.6 The Need for Consultation with Older Men

Where older men are concerned, the real challenge is not so much motivation but rather to investigate, at a deeper level, the reasons why so many men find day care centres unappealing.

Although 27 older men in total were consulted for this study, including four who did not attend day services, their comments, plus those of the service providers and PHNs, suggest that there are real difficulties in persuading older men who are in need of support and often struggling to remain in their own homes, to come to day services of any kind. This is a very important issue requiring more detailed research and analysis undertaken through in-depth consultations with older men themselves.

9.2.7 Support for Carers

One of the service objectives of day care centres is to provide support for family carers. The feedback from consultations with family carers at these centres was very positive. Most of them were caring for older people with dementia and were very pleased to have their relatives cared for, at least for a few hours every week.

The service providers and PHNs were, however, more critical of deficits in the service provided for family carers, especially where the caring caused an undue burden either through dementia or high dependency. While acknowledging that it would not be a good or necessary policy to relieve family carers of all their responsibilities and obligations, several service providers and PHNs in this sector argued for the need for increased choice for the more burdened family carers.

Even though day care centres were understaffed and under-resourced in many ways, service providers felt that by opening for only five days a week and six hours a day, they offered a poor service to family carers. This finding is supported by the social policy report on carers (Comhairle, 2002) which reported that availability and opening hours of day care centres were regarded as inadequate and did not facilitate carers wishing to return to work.

During the consultations undertaken for this study, a number of issues arose which will need to be addressed in terms of future development. These include:

- insufficient numbers of centres

- long waiting lists

- understaffing and anxiety over the loss of Community Employment schemes, FÁS and Jobs Initiative-funded jobs

- difficulties in providing quality services, particularly physiotherapy

- the reluctance of older men to attend day services.

Many social club/day centres are located in the voluntary sector. Although the health authorities have, for very good historical reasons, relied heavily on the voluntary sector, the older people and their family carers, with many of the service providers and even some of the PHNs, are not interested in making this distinction. Many felt that the ultimate responsibility for providing all day services for older people (with the possible exception of those services that are totally social, such as active retirement groups) should fall squarely with the health boards.

Although many of these voluntary services may have started out with only a social benefit mandate and may be perceived by the health authorities as 'different' to statutory day care centres, the fact is that because of the chronic lack of facilities, many social club/day centres are the only facility in the greater locality and end up providing services to, and for, a wide spectrum of older people.

The NCAOP, in noting the lack of statutory places in day services, argues that there is an obvious need for additional health board places in areas without a well-developed voluntary sector. In areas with a strong voluntary sector, there is a need for greater support from the relevant health boards towards the development of these facilities (Ruddle *et al.*, 1997).

This call from six years ago is, if anything, more applicable today than ever before. The social club/day centres are providing increasing levels of service in the areas of personal care, paramedical treatments and even nursing. They are providing relief to family carers and the safe environments needed to avail of these services. They are, in fact, fulfilling many of the classic day care objectives while, at the same time, catering for a constant flow of more active older people.

It is interesting to note that there seems to be a tendency, perhaps because of the comprehensive range of services and activities that they provide, for social club/day centres to 'go the full distance' and become the focus of 'villages' or 'campuses' for older people. Four of these centres had residential accommodation for older people on the same site or nearby, one was just about to open new accommodation and the sixth had accommodation under construction.

9.3.1 Understaffing

Despite all of these activities and plans, many of these centres were experiencing or anticipating staff shortages. In many centres, the 'key' personnel (and numbers varied) were funded directly or indirectly by the health board, but there was a reliance on FÁS, Community Employment schemes and Jobs Initiative programmes for all the other personnel who were vital to the successful delivery of services, such as cooks, drivers, cleaners and even care attendants. There is considerable anxiety in some centres over the contraction or termination of several of these schemes and a fear that proposed replacement schemes (such as the Social Economy schemes) will not be adequate.

Although it is often argued that the day of the volunteer is over, volunteering is still vital to the successful functioning of day services for older people. It is the case, however, that many volunteers (whether they are on management committees, involved in fundraising ventures or working at the 'coal face' of service delivery) are themselves older people, almost always women, whose days as volunteers are limited.

These voluntary sector services are, without doubt, contributing to the national social policy objective of supporting and maintaining older people in their own homes, in dignity, comfort, security and independence. They need greater support from the health boards, through increased funding and staff security, if they are to continue providing a high quality service, as so many of them wish to do.

9.3.2 Difficulties in Providing Certain Essential Services

In common with day care centres, the central services provided by social club/day centres should include transport, meals, personal care services and physiotherapy. Of these, the centres found it most difficult to offer a high-quality and regular physiotherapy service. The observations made above apply here equally.

9.3.3 Older Men and Their Needs

Social club/day centres have a wider range of older people attending in terms of abilities and interests and, therefore, a wider range of social activities to reflect these differences. And yet there is still a difficulty in attracting older men into the centres, as reported by the service providers, PHNs and the older men themselves. Quite a few of the centres find that when the men do come they often don't stay for long. They attend for the midday meal and the mealtime company, which they enjoy, but they don't stay in the centre for much longer than that.

These men tend to be more physically independent. They can walk or drive their own cars to the centre and the knowledge that they can come and go at any time makes it easier for them to select the services and activities they want or need and discount the rest.

For those older men who are reliant on the centre's own transport, the services and activities provided in social club/day centres do not appear to be any more attractive than those offered in day care centres. As already pointed out, this is an area that needs more investigation through consultation with older men themselves.

9.4 Developmental Issues in Dementia-Specific Day Centres

Consultations with service providers and PHNs revealed a broad range of gaps and deficits in services needed to support older people with dementia and their family carers. These include:

- insufficient numbers of dementia-specific day centres

- understaffing; the lack of cover for nurse managers; the need for more nursing support

- transport

- lack of space; cramped and overcrowded conditions; demeaning personal care facilities

- difficulties in stimulating older people with dementia; providing a suitable social activities programme, especially for those in the early stages, and for older men

- the need for more support for carers through longer opening hours and weekend opening; the particular difficulties for carers of older people with advanced dementia; the lack of services for crisis situations.

9.4.1 Insufficient Numbers of Dementia-Specific Day Centres

The service providers and PHNs consulted for this study concurred that providing day care service (as part of a package with respite care, home-sitting care, home help and meals-on-wheels) is a vitally important element in any strategy that aims to keep older people with dementia in their own homes and out of long-term residential care, for as long as is possible.

However, once more the main concern of both service providers and PHNs is the insufficient numbers of dementia-specific day centres. This is not a new observation: O'Shea and O'Reilly, in their report *An Action Plan for Dementia* (1999), discussed this issue in considerable detail. The Eastern Health Board (now the ERHA) in its *Ten Year Action Plan for Services for Older Persons 1999-2008* (1998) acknowledged that in its own area the current social support services, 'particularly day care and Public Health Nurses with time to devote to dementia sufferers', were not in adequate supply.

In Ireland it is estimated that dementia occurs in six to ten per cent of people over the age of 65 and increases to twenty per cent of those over 80 years (Kenny, 1995). At current demographic levels, with a maximum of thirty places per centre and at the lower level of risk, Ireland needs more than 980 dementia-specific day centres to provide a day service for all those over 65 years. This is clearly an impossible target and presupposes that all those over 65 years with dementia need, or want, day care. Even on the assumption that a quarter of these older people and/or their families will want day services, we are still well short of a target of 245 dementia-specific day centres.

When developing dementia-specific day centres, personal care and the suitability of the physical environment for that care are areas that require particular consideration. The two dementia-specific day centres visited for this study contrasted enormously in the facilities available for personal care. In one they were excellent but in the second the service providers described them as 'demeaning'. Up to one third of people with dementia suffer from incontinence, rising in both incidence and severity with age. For older people with dementia, particularly those in the early stages, this problem is embarrassing and should not be exacerbated by submitting them to demeaning toilet, shower and changing facilities which are an affront to their dignity. The physical environment of day centres for older people with dementia needs to be carefully designed, in keeping with best practice.

The development of dementia-specific day centres should follow the proposals and recommendations in *An Action Plan for Dementia* (O'Shea and O'Reilly, 1999), specifically its recommendation that dementia-specific day places be provided in each district of a community care area, in buildings suitable for people with dementia and with staff who are trained in their care.

9.4.2 Support for Carers

Caring for older people with dementia is much more onerous and demanding than most other forms of caring. Carers face the challenges of constant supervision, unpredictable and aggressive behaviour, and wandering. There are also difficulties associated with personal care such as eating, hygiene and incontinence. All of these can place an enormous strain on a carer, especially if, as is often the case, the carer is also an older person. Many older people with dementia under the age of eighty, have their spouse as their primary or sole family carer.

The service providers and PHNs consulted for this study were acutely aware of the cost to a family carer's own physical and psychological health. They were aware that carers are very often so burdened that they have no time to nurture their own needs or those of other family members. They were also aware that all too often the burden of caring for a parent with dementia can fall entirely on the shoulders of one child, with no support from any other member of the family. For many of the carers, not only is work outside the home impossible – all activities outside the home are impossible.

The concept of a social club or active retirement group, with accompanying objectives, is not perhaps a very well developed one as yet. Although *The Years Ahead* (Department of Health, 1988) recommended a ratio of one social club per 600 older people, 'social clubs', as distinct from 'day care centres' and 'day centres', are barely mentioned in *The Years Ahead Report: A Review of the Implementation of its Recommendations* (Ruddle *et al.*, 1997).

There is a general lack of reference in health and social policy to the role and functions of social clubs or active retirement groups. In describing opportunities for health promotion for older people, Brenner and Shelley (1998) suggest a variety of locations, but make no mention of social clubs or active retirement groups.

The one social club examined as part of this study was fundamentally different to all the other centres visited (see Chapter Seven) and was at odds with the image of social clubs as conveyed through policy documents. This social club, despite funding uncertainties and infrastructural drawbacks, is positively bristling with aims and objectives, programmes and activities, plans and ambitions.

As a model of how to challenge and question the barriers of old age and as a model of health promotion and healthy ageing, this centre can be an inspiration to all, and should be treated as an equal component in the continuum of day services for older people.

This social club extends limits and it challenges the usual stereotypes of what older people can, will and want to do. There is no doubt that this service demonstrates the benefits to be derived from a social model of service, aiming at and responding to the needs and preferences of active older people as well as the more dependent. This example strongly supports the case for secure statutory core funding so that a centre such as this one is able to meet its objectives.

180

References

References

Bacon, P., 2001. *Current and Future Supply and Demand Conditions in the Labour Market for Certain Professional Therapists.* Dublin: Stationery Office.

Barnes, M., 1994. *Seeking Representative Views from Frail Older People.* Edinburgh: Age Concern Scotland.

Bauld, L., Chesterman, J. and Judge, K., 2000. 'Measuring Satisfaction with Social Care amongst Older Service Users: Issues from the Literature' *Health and Social Care in the Community*, Vol. 8(5): 316-324.

Blackman, T., Brodhurst, S. and Convery, J. (eds), 2001. *Social Care and Social Exclusion: a Comparative Study of Older People's Care in Europe.* Basingstoke: Palgrave.

Brenner, H. and Shelley, E., 1998. *Adding Years to Life and Life to Years: a Health Promotion Strategy for Older People.* Dublin: National Council on Ageing and Older People.

Central Statistics Office, 2001. *The Projected Growth in the Number of People with Dementia in Ireland, 2001-2026.* Dublin: Central Statistics Office.

Clark, C. (ed), 2001. *Adult Day Services and Social Inclusion: Better Days.* London: Jessica Kingsley Publishers.

Comhairle, 2002. *Supporting Carers: Social Policy Series.* Dublin: Comhairle.

Convery, J., 1987. *Choices in Community Care: Day Centres for the Elderly in the Eastern Health Board.* Dublin: National Council for the Aged.

Convery, J., 2001a. 'Social Inclusion of Older People in the Health and Social Services in Ireland' in McGivern, Y. (ed). *Towards a Society for All Ages.* Dublin: National Council on Ageing and Older People.

Convery, J., 2001b. 'Ireland' in Blackman, T. (ed). *Social Care and Social Exclusion: a Comparative Study of Older People's Care in Europe.* Hampshire: Palgrave, 83-95.

Delaney, S., Garavan, R., McGee, H. and Tynan, A., 2001. *Care and Case Management for Older People in Ireland.* Dublin: National Council on Ageing and Older People.

Department of Health and Children, 2001. *Quality and Fairness: A Health System for You.* Dublin: Stationery Office.

Department of Health, 1988. *The Years Ahead: A Policy for the Elderly.* Dublin: Stationery Office.

Department of Health, 1994. *Shaping a Healthier Future: A Strategy for Effective Healthcare in the 1990s.* Dublin: Stationery Office.

Donabedian, A., 1966. 'Evaluating the Quality of Medical Care' *Milbank Memorial Fund Quarterly: Health and Safety,* Vol. 44 (3): 166-203.

Donabedian, A., 1988. 'The Quality of Care. How Can it Be Assessed?' *Journal of the American Medical Association,* Vol.260: 1743–1748.

Eastern Health Board, 1998. *Ten Year Action Plan for Services for Older Persons 1999-2008.* Dublin: Stationery Office.

Eastern Regional Health Authority, 2001. *Review of the Implementation of the Ten Year Action Plan for Services for Older People 1999-2008.* Dublin: Stationery Office.

Equality Authority, 2002. *Implementing Equality for Older People.* Dublin: Equality Authority.

Garavan, R., Winder, R. and McGee, H., 2001. *Health and Social Services for Older People (HeSSOP).* Dublin: National Council on Ageing and Older People.

Government of Ireland, 1999. *Ireland: National Development Plan 2000-2006.* Dublin: Stationery Office.

Government of Ireland, 2000. *Programme for Prosperity and Fairness.* Dublin: Stationery Office.

Harding, T., 1997. *A Life Worth Living: The Independence and Inclusion of Older People.* London: Help the Aged.

Haslett, D., Ruddle, H. and Hennessy, G., 1998. *The Future Organisation of the Home Help Service In Ireland.* Dublin: National Council on Ageing and Older People.

Hunter, S. and Watt, G., 2001. 'Trends and Aspirations in Day Services for Older People', in Clark, C. (ed), *Adult Day Services and Social Inclusion: Better Days.* London: Jessica Kingsley Publishers.

Kenny, G., 1995. *Take Good Care of Yourself: Growing Old in Ireland.* Dublin: Gill and Macmillan.

Kerry Community Services, 2002. D*ay Care Centres: Operational Policies: Draft Report.*

Layte, R., Fahey, T. and Whelan, C., 1999. *Income, Deprivation and Well-being among Older Irish People.* Dublin: National Council on Ageing and Older People.

Loftus, M., 2001. 'Chairperson's Address' in McGivern, Y. (ed), *Towards a Society for All Ages.* Dublin: National Council on Ageing and Older People.

MacDonald, C., 1999. *Support at Home: Views of Older People on Their Needs and Access to Services.* Edinburgh: The Stationery Office.

McAvoy, H., 2001. *A Prospective Comparative Study of the Influence of Day Care on the Quality of Life and Health of Older People.* National University of Galway: unpublished thesis.

McCartney, C., 1992. *The Promise of Evaluation: What Evaluation Offers Policy-makers and Practitioners.* Coleraine: University of Ulster.

McNamara, C., 1999. *Basic Guide to Program Evaluation.* Minnesota: Management Assistance Programme for Non-profit Organisations.

Midland Health Board, ongoing. *Review of Day Care Services. Draft Report.*

Moffatt, T., 2000. *Department of Health and Children Press Release, November 24, 2000.*

National Council on Ageing and Older People, 2001. *Pre-budget Submission.* Dublin: National Council on Ageing and Older People.

National Working Group on Performance Indicators, 2002. *Glossary of Terms: Services for Older Persons*. Dublin: Stationery Office.

Nocon, A., Qureshi, H. and Thornton, P., 1997. *Outcomes in Community Care Practice: the Perspective of Users' and Carers' Organisations*. University of York: Social Policy Research Unit.

Ombudsman's Report, 2001. *The Nursing Home Subvention Scheme*. Dublin: Stationery Office.

O'Shea, E. and O'Reilly, S., 1999. *An Action Plan for Dementia*. Dublin: National Council on Ageing and Older People.

Owens, D.J. and Batchelor, C.,1996. 'Patient Satisfaction and the Elderly' *Social Science and Medicine*, Vol. 42: 1843-1491.

Pope, C. and Mays, N., 1993. 'Opening the Black Box: An Encounter in the Corridors of Health Service Research' *British Medical Journal*, 306, 315.

Raynes, N., Temple, B., Glenister, C. and Coulthard, L., 2001. *Quality at Home for Older People: Involving Service Users in Defining Home Care Specifications*. London: The Policy Press.

Report of the Working Group on Elder Abuse, 2002. *Protecting Our Future*. Dublin: Stationery Office.

Ruddle, H. and Mulvihill, R., 1999. *Reaching Out: Charitable Giving and Volunteering in the Republic of Ireland*. Dublin: National College of Ireland.

Ruddle, H., Donoghue, F. and Mulvihill, R., 1997. *The Years Ahead Report: A Review of the Implementation of its Recommendations*. Dublin: National Council on Ageing and Older People.

South Eastern Health Board, 2000. *Listening to the Voice of Carers: An Exploration of the Health and Social Care Needs and Experiences of Informal Carers of Older People*. South Eastern Health Board.

Tester, S., 1996. *Community Care for Older People: a Comparative Perspective*. London: Macmillan.

Tester, S., 2001. 'Day Services for Older People' in Clark C. (ed), *Adult Day Services and Social Inclusion: Better Days*. London: Jessica Kingsley Publishers.

Western Health Board, 2001. *Health and Well-being for Older People: a Strategy for 2001-2006*. Western Health Board.

186

Appendices

187

Appendix A: Additional Findings

Additional Findings for Older People Who Attended Day Facilities

Percentage of older men and older women in each age category (numbers in brackets)

Age	Men	Women
69 and under	30% (3)	70% (7)
70 - 74	35% (8)	65% (15)
75 - 79	33% (6)	67% (12)
80 - 84	22% (4)	78% (14)
85 - 89	25% (2)	75% (6)
90 and over	0% (0)	100% (1)
Total	30% (23)	70% (55)

Percentage of older people in each marital category by living circumstances (numbers in brackets)*

	Single	Married	Widowed
Living alone	25% (8)	6% (2)	69% (22)
Living with family members	8% (3)	45% (17)	47% (18)
Other arrangement	0% (0)	0% (0)	4% (100)
Total	15% (11)	26% (19)	59% (44)

* Although all the older people were asked the same questions, in some cases, for one reason or another, they did not wish to answer. This explains why, in a few of the tables, the totals do not add up to 78.

Percentage of older people by means of travel to day facility (numbers in brackets)

Public transport	1% (1)
Family transport	14% (11)
Neighbour/friend transport	4% (3)
Voluntary organisation supplies transport	35% (27)
Statutory organisation supplies transport	15% (12)
Other arrangement (e.g. walk, own car)	31% (24)
Total	100% (78)

Percentage of older people attending by number of days per week (numbers in brackets)

One day a week	32% (23)
2-3 days a week	24% (17)
4-5 days a week	37% (27)
6-7 days a week	0% (0)
Less than one day a week	7% (5)
Total	100% (72)

Percentage of older people who would like to attend more days each week (numbers in brackets)

Yes	31% (21)
No	65% (44)
Sometimes	4% (3)
Total	100% (68)

Percentage of older people by hours per day attending day facility (numbers in brackets)

Up to 2 hours	4% (3)
More than 2 and up to 4	15% (11)
More than 4 and up to 6	76% (55)
More than 6	1% (1)
Other variation	3% (2)
Total	**100% (72)**

Percentage of older people by level of enjoyment in coming to centre (numbers in brackets)

Very high	78% (59)
High	14% (11)
Just alright	8% (6)
Low/very low	0% (0)
Total	**100% (76)**

Percentage of older people's self-assessed physical health * (numbers in brackets)

Very good	35% (27)
Good	13% (10)
Just alright	20% (16)
Poor	17% (13)
Very poor	15% (12)
Total	**100% (78)**

Percentage of older people's self-assessed mental health * (numbers in brackets)

Very good	53% (41)
Good	26% (20)
Just alright	10% (8)
Poor	6% (5)
Very poor	5% (4)
Total	**100% (78)**

Percentage of older people's self-assessed economic circumstances * (numbers in brackets)

Very good	38% (30)
Good	37% (29)
Just alright	22% (17)
Poor	3% (2)
Total	**100% (78)**

* In a very small number of cases, where the older person had difficulties making self-assessments, the judgement of the manager of the centre was sought.

Additional Findings for Older People Who Did Not Attend Day Facilities

Numbers of older men and older women in each age category

Age	Men	Women
69 and under	1	0
70 - 74	0	2
75 - 79	2	5
80 - 84	0	8
85 - 89	0	3
90 and over	0	1
Unknown	1	0
Total	**4**	**19**

Percentage of older people in each marital category by living circumstances (numbers in brackets)

	Single	Married	Widowed
Living alone	18% (2)	9% (1)	73% (8)
Living with family	29% (2)	71% (5)	0% (0)
Other arrangement	50% (1)	0% (0)	50% (1)
Total	25% (5)	30% (6)	45% (9)

Percentage of older people's self-assessed physical health (numbers in brackets)

Very good	31% (7)
Good	4% (1)
Just alright	39% (9)
Poor	13% (3)
Very poor	13% (3)
Total	100% (23)

Percentage of older people's self-assessed mental health (numbers in brackets)

Very good	57% (13)
Good	30% (7)
Just alright	9% (2)
Poor	4% (1)
Total	100% (23)

Percentage of older people's self-assessed economic circumstances (numbers in brackets)

Very good	35% (8)
Good	26% (6)
Just alright	30% (7)
Poor	9% (2)
Total	100% (23)

Appendix B: Social Activities

The range of social activities across the fifteen facilities in the study was diverse, including:

- aromatherapy

- art and painting

- bingo

- computer classes

- conversation

- crafts

- crosswords

- dancing

- drama

- games including bingo, bowling and cards

- gardening

- gentle exercises

- giving knitting classes in local schools

- indoor bowling

- Keep-fit classes

- music including sing-songs, dancing, playing an instrument or listening to visiting volunteer musicians

- patchwork

- watching and discussing old-time videos

- reading papers, magazines and books

- running a second hand clothes shop

- running a telephone helpline

- senior sports

- spiritual services

- trips and outings

- writing poetry.

Terms of Reference

Terms of Reference

The National Council on Ageing and Older People was established on 19th March 1997 in succession to the National Council for the Elderly (January 1990 to March 1997) and the National Council for the Aged (June 1981 to January 1990).

The functions of the Council are as follows:

1. To advise the Minister for Health and Children on all aspects of ageing and the welfare of older people, either at its own initiative or at the request of the Minister and in particular on:

   a) measures to promote the health of older people;

   b) measures to promote the social inclusion of older people;

   c) the implementation of the recommendations contained in policy reports commissioned by the Minister for Health;

   d) methods of ensuring co-ordination between public bodies at national and local level in the planning and provision of services for older people;

   e) methods of encouraging greater partnership between statutory and voluntary bodies in providing services for older people;

   f) meeting the needs of the most vulnerable older people;

   g) means of encouraging positive attitudes to life after 65 years and the process of ageing;

   h) means of encouraging greater participation by older people;

   i) whatever action, based on research, is required to plan and develop services for older people.

2. To assist the development of national and regional policies and strategies designed to produce health gain and social gain for older people by:

   a) undertaking research on the lifestyle and the needs of older people in Ireland;

   b) identifying and promoting models of good practice in the care of older people and service delivery to them;

   c) providing information and advice based on research findings to those involved in the development and/or implementation of policies and services pertaining to the health, well-being and autonomy of older people;

   d) liaising with statutory, voluntary and professional bodies involved in the development and/or implementation of national and regional policies which have as their object health gain or social gain for older people.

3. To promote the health, welfare and autonomy of older people.

4. To promote a better understanding of ageing and older people in Ireland.

5. To liaise with international bodies which have functions similar to the functions of the Council.

The Council may also advise other Ministers, at their request, on aspects of ageing and the welfare of older people which are within the functions of the Council.

Membership